Technical Award in Health & Social Care

Judith Adams

Orders: please contact Bookpoint Ltd, 130 Park Drive, Milton Park, Abingdon, Oxon OX14 4SE. Telephone: +44 (0)1235 827827. Fax: +44 (0)1235 400401. Email education@bookpoint.co.uk Lines are open from 9 a.m. to 5 p.m., Monday to Saturday, with a 24-hour message answering service. You can also order through our website: www.hoddereducation.co.uk

ISBN: 9781510462151

First published in 2019 by
Hodder Education,
An Hachette UK Company
Carmelite House
50 Victoria Embankment
London EC4Y 0DZ

www.hoddereducation.co.uk

Impression number 10 9 8 7 6 5 4 3 2 1

Year 2023 2022 2021 2020 2019

Illustrations by Integra Software Services Pvt. Ltd., Pondicherry, India

Typeset in India by Integra Software Services Pvt. Ltd., Pondicherry, India

Printed in Italy

A catalogue record for this title is available from the British Library.

CONTENTS

Acknowledgements

Author's acknowledgements

A special thank you to the team at Hodder for their support and insightful guidance, especially Stephen Halder and Imogen Miles; also Rebecca Norman and the other editors involved in the production of this book.

To my husband Tony, for your never-ending support and encouragement.

Picture credits

The Publishers would like to thank the following for permission to reproduce copyright material.

Page 1 © michaeljung/stock.adobe.com; page 17 © wavebreakmedia/Shutterstock.com; page 19 © Photofusion Picture Library / Alamy Stock Photo; page 20 © Monkey Business/stock.adobe.com; page 28 © Barry Barnes / 123RF; page 31 © Cathy Yeulet/123RF.com; page 38 © Igor Zakowski / Shutterstock; page 42 © Monkey Business/stock.adobe.com; page 49 © WavebreakmediaMicro/stock.adobe.com; page 51 © WavebreakmediaMicro/stock.adobe.com; page 56 © Jacob Lund/stock.adobe.com; page 76 © ALPA PROD/Shutterstock.com; page 96 © Monkey Business/stock.adobe.com; page 102 © Odua Images/stock.adobe.com; page 104 © Rungaroon taweeapiradeemunkohg/123RF; page 106 © Arto/stock.adobe.com; page 109 © macrovector/123RF; page 112 © Monkey Business/stock.adobe.com; page 113 © Monkey Business/stock.adobe.com; page 114 © Science History Images / Alamy Stock Photo; page 116 © Kirill Zdorov - Fotolia; page 137 © WavebreakmediaMicro/stock.adobe.com

How to use this book

Key features of the book

High priority

Make sure you know:

- the purpose of care planning
- how individualised care planning meets holistic needs
- the stages in the care planning cycle.

The most important things to focus on

Jargon buster

Care Quality Commission (CQC) – a government organisation responsible for checking standards in health and social care settings.

Understand the meaning of important terms

Theory in action

Serena is nearly six months pregnant. So far, she has not bothered to attend any antenatal care appointments. She enjoys smoking and likes to go out for a drink at weekends with her friends. Describe the potential impact of Serena's lifestyle on the development of her unborn baby.

Real-life situations that show how theory links to practice

My life as a sonographer

My role is to carry out ultrasound scans to check how the baby is developing and to check for any abnormalities. I play an important role in the lives of my patients. I am with them as they hear their baby's heart beat for the first time. I help the doctors diagnose and treat disease. I also provide support to patients during what can be very emotional circumstances.

Finding out the roles of different health and social care professionals

Activity

Explain why this goal is not SMART: 'I will complete my work for my project by tomorrow evening.'

Practical tasks to support your learning

Find out more about

Occupational therapy

Use the link below to watch a clip of an NHS occupational therapist explaining what her job involves.

www.nhs.uk/video/Pages/Occupationaltherapy.aspx

Tasks that involve further reading or research

Read and write

1. Find a job advertisement for a health and social care role you are interested in.
2. Read the information provided then write a detailed job description for that role.

Tasks to help your literacy skills

Five things to know

Care needs and life stages

Make sure you know:

1. the names of the six different life stages
2. a brief description of each life stage
3. care needs that all infants will have
4. unexpected care needs that could occur at any life stage
5. care needs created by a long-term illness.

Essential points within a section

Extend

Find out more about the Care Certificate and see how the 6Cs are a part of each of the 15 Care Certificate standards.

Increase your depth of knowledge

Check what you know

Describe four general skills and four specialist skills needed to be a nurse.

Making sure that you can remember keep points

Introduction

The aim of this book is to help you to develop the knowledge, understanding and practical skills that you will need to complete your CACHE Level 2 Technical Award in Health and Social Care qualification. This qualification will provide you with an introduction to the topics, issues and legislation that it is important to be aware of when working in health and social care settings. For up-to-date information about the qualification, visit www.cache.org.uk.

Each of the sections in this book closely follow all the topics required for each unit in the course specification. 'High priority' concepts are clearly identified and defined throughout the text and how each topic applies in practice is shown through 'Theory in action' features.

Mandatory units

All students will need to complete:

- Unit TAHSC1 Introduction to the health and social care sector
- Unit TAHSC2 Professional practice and the health and social care practitioner
- Unit TAHSC3 Human growth and development through the life stages

These are referred to as Units 1, 2 and 3 throughout this book.

Assessment

The assessment consists of one scenario-based short-answer examination and three internal assessments.

Scenario-based short-answer examination

- The examination is set and marked by CACHE. It is graded Pass, Merit or Distinction.
- The scenario-based examination is based on knowledge and understanding from the content of all three units and so is called 'synoptic'.
- It is worth 45.5 per cent of the qualification grade.

Internal assessments

- Each mandatory unit will be internally marked using assessment grading criteria.
- The assignments are marked by your tutor and then externally quality assured by CACHE.

All of the examination questions and assignment tasks contain 'command' verbs that tell you what you have to do to answer the question or complete the task. Example command verbs might be to 'explain', 'summarise', 'describe' or 'identify'. Definitions of the command verbs are shown at the end of this introduction. Always check the command verb before starting a task or answering a question. If you describe something when an explanation is required you will not be able to gain full marks; this is because an explanation requires more detail than a description.

Plagiarism and referencing

Your work for the unit assignment assessment tasks must be in your own words. You must not plagiarise. Plagiarism is the submission of another's work as your own and/or failure to acknowledge a source correctly. Sometimes you might need to use a diagram or include a quotation from someone else, such as a reference from this book. If you do this it is very important that you always provide a reference for any information you use, to make it clear that it is not your own work. Quotation marks should be placed around any quoted text. You should put the source reference next to the information used. In addition to referencing the picture, diagram, table or quotation, you should explain in your own words why you have used it, what it tells you and how it relates to your work.

Providing a reference means that you will give details of the source, i.e. where you found the information. You should include the full website address and date you found the information or, for a textbook, the author's name, date the book published, title and the name of the publisher. For example, 'Adams, J. (2019), *CACHE Level 2 Technical Award in Health and Social Care*, Hodder Education'. For newspaper or magazine articles you should give the date of publication, title of the paper or magazine and the name of the author. When producing your work for the assessment you should not use a template or writing frame; you must always decide yourself how to present your information.

It is also good practice to include a bibliography at the end of your assignment. A bibliography is a list of all the sources of information you have used, whether for background reading, quotations used in your work, or possibly an individual you have interviewed. The bibliography shows how detailed your research has been for the assignment and demonstrates how you have found the information needed to complete your assignment.

Glossary of terms used at Level 2

Term	Definition
Compare and contrast	Examine the subject in detail looking at similarities and differences.
Consider	Think carefully and write about a problem, action or decision.
Create	Produce new ideas and solutions.
Define	State the meaning of a word or phrase.
Describe	Write about the subject giving detailed information.
Explain	Provide details about the subject with reasons showing how or why. Some responses could include examples.
Give (examples, information, facts)	Provide relevant examples to support the subject.
Identify	List or name the main points.
List	Make a list of key words, sentences or comments that focus on the subject.
Outline	Identify or describe the main points.
Summarise	Give the main ideas or facts in a concise way.
Use	Take or apply an item, resource or piece of information as asked in the question or task.

Introduction to the health and social care sector

About this unit

This unit gives you the opportunity to explore the different types of health and social care provision available for individuals. You will learn about the job roles of a range of health and social care practitioners. You will also gain an insight into the ways different services work together to meet the needs of individuals at different life stages.

You will find out about the difficulties, or 'barriers', that may stop individuals from accessing services and examine how care providers can help to overcome those difficulties so that individuals receive the care they need.

You will also learn how regulatory bodies such as the Care Quality Commission and Ofsted monitor and influence the quality of services provided by the health and social care sector.

Assessment of learning grid

Grade	Learning outcome	Assessment of learning
P1	1	**Identify** one (1) example of a health and social care service from each of the following types of provision that can be found in your local area: • statutory • private • voluntary. **List** the functions of each of the services identified.
P2	2	**Describe** one (1) health and social care job role held within each of the services identified in P1: • statutory • private • voluntary.
P3	3	**Identify** two (2) types of referral used to access health and social care services.
P4	3	**Explain** how three (3) barriers to accessing health and social care services may be overcome.
P5	4	**Outline** one (1) health and social care service typically accessed at each life stage.
P6	5	**Give** two (2) examples of informal care.
P7	6	**Describe** the role of regulatory and inspection bodies for health and social care.
M1	1	**Describe** the functions of one (1) type of health and social care service from each of the following: • statutory provision • private provision • voluntary provision.
M2	3	**Explain** two (2) types of referral used to access health and social care services.
M3	4	**Explain** how health and social care services meet the care needs of individuals at each life stage.
D1	5	**Compare and contrast** formal and informal care services.
D2	6	**Explain** the impact of regulatory inspection on: • individuals accessing health and social care • the service provider • public trust.

Learning outcome 1: Understand health and social care provision (P1, M1)

High priority

Make sure you know:

- the meaning of the key terms 'statutory', 'private' and 'voluntary'
- examples of health and social care services
- functions of health and social care services.

1.1 Types of health and social care services

Care provision means the different types of care services that are available for **clients/service users** or **client groups**. Health care is the organised provision of medical care and it aims to prevent, diagnose and treat illness, injury and disease. Social care services support **individuals** with their daily lives. Examples include providing for personal care needs, such as preparing meals or washing and dressing, that the individual cannot manage by themselves due to illness, disability or old age and supporting children and families or vulnerable adults in the **local** community. Social care also includes adoption and foster care services.

Jargon buster

Client or **service user** – an individual who accesses a health or social care service.

Client group – a group of individuals accessing a health or social care service.

Individual – a person, man, woman or child accessing health or social care.

Local – refers to a particular area.

Statutory health and social care services

Statutory services are **national** services that must be provided by law throughout the UK. The laws that state this are called 'statutes' and so this is where the word 'statutory' comes from. The government sets up, manages and leads statutory services. They are funded (paid for) from working people's taxes based on their income. The National Health Service (NHS) and local authorities are examples of statutory provision that are legally required to be provided by the government. NHS England oversees the funding, planning and delivery of the NHS, for example. Clinical **commissioning** groups are responsible for planning and providing the health and care services that are needed in their local area.

Table 1.1 Examples of statutory health and social care services

Health care services	Social care services
Accident and emergency departments (A&E)	Day centres
Ambulance service	**Domiciliary care**
Child psychology services	Family support centres
Family planning services	Fostering and adoption services
GPs (General Practitioners)	Learning disability services
Health centres	Residential care homes
Hospitals	Residential nursing homes
Maternity services	Safeguarding services
Mental and social health services	
Occupational therapy	
Pharmacies	

Private health and social care services

Private services are owned or run by private individuals rather than the government. Private care providers usually charge a fee for their services as they are businesses and need to make a profit. Examples include private residential care homes, BUPA and Nuffield Health Hospitals, non-NHS dentists, private day nurseries and opticians. Some of the services they provide may not be available in the statutory sector.

Jargon buster

Commissioning – the process of planning and agreeing services that are needed.

Domiciliary care – care and support provided for an individual in their own home (also known as home care).

National – refers to the whole country.

Check what you know

Are the following health and social care services 'statutory' or 'private' or both?

1 An NHS hospital
2 A pharmacy
3 A residential nursing home
4 A local authority day centre

Voluntary health and social care services

These are not-for-profit organisations and charities and are sometimes referred to as third-sector organisations. Although some staff will be paid to lead and manage the organisation (usually from income received in the form of donations or grants), services are mainly provided by volunteers who do not get paid and who give their time for free. These services are not run by the government and they do not have a statutory duty to provide services. Instead they provide health and social care services because they see a need for them.

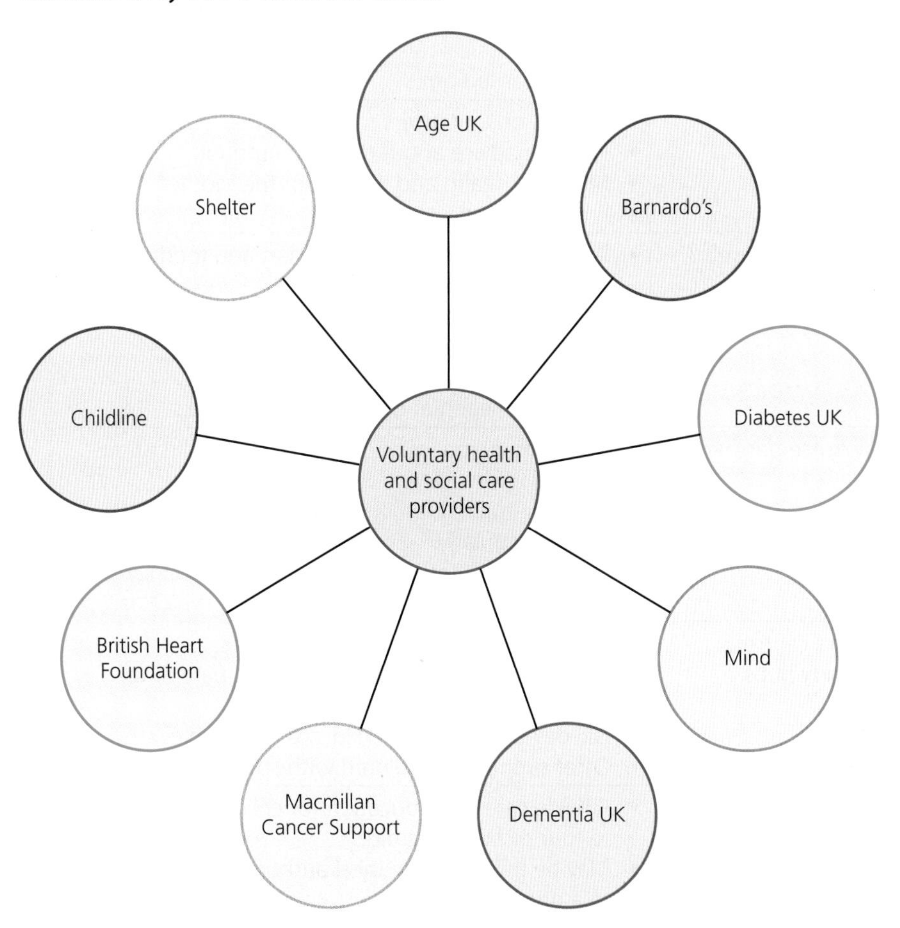

Figure 1.1 Examples of voluntary health and social care providers

Find out more

Look at the websites of the voluntary organisations shown in Figure 1.1. Read about the different types of services and support they provide.

Check what you know

Write a definition of 'statutory', private' and 'voluntary' health and social care services.

Theory in action

Read the information in Table 1.2 about different types of services available to support parents and carers of babies and children.

Table 1.2 Health and social care services for families

Type of service	Support offered
Child health monitoring	• At the GP surgery baby will be weighed regularly (once a month up to age six months, then every two months up to age one year, then every three months). • Regular physical health and development checks will be carried out.
Health visitor	• Advises on and offers support with breastfeeding. • Provides advice about diet and nutrition. • Monitors health and welfare of the mother. • Provides postnatal care.
Child health or 'well baby' clinics	• Run mother and baby and parent and toddler sessions. • Offer breastfeeding support clinics. • Run peer support groups. • Administer immunisations. • Carry out health and development checks.
Family nurse partnership	• Voluntary home visiting programme for first-time parents under 24 years old. • Specially-trained family nurse visits the young mother regularly. • Helps the mother to have a healthy pregnancy and plan her future.
Children's centres/ community hubs	• Linked to statutory maternity services. • Provide advice and information, e.g. parenting classes, benefits advice. • Full day or temporary childcare is available. • Offer support for children with special needs.
Nurseries	• Provide care and education for children from birth to four or five years old. • May be privately run, local authority run or attached to a primary school.

Activity

1 Do some research and find out about the range of health and social care services that are available for families in your area.

2 Are each of the services statutory, private or voluntary?

1.2 Functions of health and social care services

There are many different functions of health and social care services. Nationally, NHS England aims to improve the population's quality of life by providing the care, support and treatment that is needed. Prevention of ill health and the promotion of healthy living lifestyles are also key priorities for national health and social care provision. Clinical commissioning groups provide services needed by individuals in a local area, matching the services provided to the needs of the local population.

Meeting long-term and short-term needs

Health and social care services have to be available to meet a wide range of different care needs. A serious illness might mean that someone has long-term care needs that require medical and social care for the rest of their life, for example an individual with chronic lung disease or heart disease may have ongoing medical and social care needs.

Other individuals may have care needs that are only temporary. Following an operation an individual may have a short-term need for social care, for example help with daily living tasks such as getting dressed, preparing a meal or taking and picking up a child from nursery. Once they have fully recovered from the operation the need for medical care and extra social care and support ends. Another example of when short-term care might be needed is where a child is provided with emergency foster care if their primary carer is taken ill and there are no other family members to look after their child.

Residential care provision

There are many different types of residential care that provide for a range of different client groups. For example, older adults who only need support with daily living tasks, younger adults with learning or physical disabilities and residential homes for children of all ages who may have physical, emotional or learning difficulties.

- **Residential care home** – a care setting where individuals have their own room within a shared building. A care home also provides communal areas such as a dining room, sitting room and gardens. Residential care homes are staffed 24 hours a day and provide meals, personal care, cleaning, laundry services and daily activities.
- **Nursing homes** – these provide medical care as well as personal care and the staff will include qualified nurses. Some residential care homes include nursing care to specialise in conditions such as dementia care.

- **Supported living** – this is where individuals live independently in their own home but are provided with support. For example, an individual with a learning disability could live independently in a supported living flat and receive help with money management, household tasks and making healthy living choices.
- **Sheltered accommodation (sometimes known as extra care accommodation)** – individuals live in their own self-contained flat which they may own or rent. There are also communal areas such as a lounge, and some also have a restaurant and gardens. The accommodation is warden controlled meaning that there is always someone on duty who can be contacted by the residents if they need support.

Find out more

Sheltered housing

Look at the Age UK website to research sheltered housing.

www.ageuk.org.uk/information-advice/care/housing-options/sheltered-housing

Write a summary of the information you find.

Five things to know

Care provision

1. A residential care home provides accommodation, meals, activities, help with daily living tasks and personal care.
2. A nursing home provides medical and nursing care in addition to everything a residential care home provides.
3. Care homes of any type can be private or statutory providers.
4. Private care services charge for the care they provide.
5. Voluntary organisations are non-profit-making providers and do not charge for their services.

Respite provision

Respite care provision is time limited and temporary. For example, it may be provided for the caregivers of a child or adult. Respite breaks can be planned or unplanned, such as in the case of an emergency. Respite provision gives carers the opportunity to have a break from their caring duties. They are able to spend some time looking after their own needs, safe in the knowledge that their loved one is being looked after properly by professionals.

Community care provision

Community care services are intended to help individuals who require care and support to live with dignity and independence in their community and to avoid social isolation. The client groups include older adults and individuals who have mental illness, a learning disability or a physical disability.

The main aim of providing community care services is to enable individuals to continue living in their own home and to remain as independent as possible. The local authority arranges and provides community care services, although sometimes community care can be provided by volunteers or purchased by service users from private businesses.

Table 1.3 Examples of community care services

Type of service	Examples
Home care help with personal care tasks	Bathing, washing, getting up and out of bed, going to bed, getting dressed, shopping.
Home helps	Help with general tasks in the home such as cooking and cleaning, maintaining hygiene in the home.
Adaptions in the home	Provision of a stair lift, lowering worktops in the kitchen for wheelchair users, or more minor adaptions such as handrails in the bathroom and a ramp at the front door.
Meals	Daily meal delivery service – 'meals on wheels' or a monthly delivery of frozen meals. Providing meals at a day centre or lunch club.
Activities	Providing transport to attend day centres, lectures, outings and cultural activities.

Rehabilitation

Rehabilitation services are specialist services that aim to improve or maintain an individual's independence during and after an illness or after an accident. For example, individuals who have had a stroke or been injured in a car accident and lost the use of an arm or leg, or whose speech has been impaired, may require the following rehabilitation services:

- An occupational therapist to help the individual to learn techniques enabling them to wash, get dressed or prepare a meal. The therapy may include learning how to use equipment to manage physical problems or exercises to restore strength and improve the use of the affected arm or leg.
- A physiotherapist to help develop and improve mobility, such as getting from bed to a chair and exercises to improve balance and co-ordination.
- A speech and language therapist to provide help and support to try and improve or regain speech.

Specific service provision to meet needs

Some services offer specialised care and support for the particular needs of different client groups in the community. Examples include sports injury clinics, alcohol and drug addiction clinics, maternity services, dementia care and mental health services. Some more detailed examples are described below.

Maternity services

- Antenatal care including midwife-led check-ups, classes and information sessions to attend before the baby is born, for example about how to be healthy during pregnancy, what to expect during labour and how to feed and look after the baby.
- Postnatal care/health visitor service is provided after the baby is born and includes checks carried out on the health and wellbeing of mother and baby.
- Special care baby unit provides intensive care for premature babies who have been born earlier than expected.
- Well baby clinic carries out regular checks on baby's growth and developmental progress.

Mental health services

- Counselling and other services provided for individuals who may have specific emotional needs due to, for example, a traumatic experience.
- Specialised help for those with an eating disorder.
- An individual with Alzheimer's disease may need constant 24-hour care in a nursing home that specialises in dementia.

Alcohol and drug addiction clinics

- These clinics may be provided by the NHS, by private clinics where individuals pay for services themselves and by charity organisations such as Addaction.
- Service users will attend a programme of intensive support at a local clinic or a residential rehabilitation service.

Hospice care

- A form of care that aims to improve the lives of people who have an incurable illness, as well as providing support for the patient's family and carers.
- Care is free, paid for by a combination of NHS funding and public donations.
- A hospice provides pain and symptom control.
- A hospice provides holistic care by supporting the patient's emotional and social needs as well as their physical care.

Activity

Find out about the different types of community care provision that are available in your area for:

- an adult with a learning disability
- a 16-year-old with a physical disability
- an 87-year-old who lives in their own home, who requires help with daily living tasks.

Five things to know

Health and social care services

1. Community care services aim to enable individuals to continue living in their own home and to remain as independent as possible, for as long as possible.
2. Some care services, such as bathing, dressing and preparing a meal, can be provided in a client's own home.
3. Specialist care services are provided in hospitals, clinics and GP surgeries and by the local authority.
4. Well baby clinics are part of maternity services and assess a baby's growth and development.
5. Hospice care aims to improve the lives of people who have an incurable illness; care is funded partly by the NHS and partly by voluntary donations.

Learning outcome 2: Understand job roles of health and social care practitioners (P2)

High priority

Make sure you know:

- the general skills and competency requirements for health and social care practitioners
- examples of the specialist skills required for a range of job roles in health and social care services.

2.1 Job roles within the health and social care sector

Many of the huge range of different job roles within the health and social care sector require specialist skills and training. However, all job roles require the same general skills, behaviours and attributes and examples of some of these are described in Table 1.4.

Table 1.4 General competency skills needed by health and social care practitioners

Skill/behaviour/attribute	Examples
English skills	• Writing a care plan • Reading a risk assessment • Reporting an incident • Updating patient records
Numeracy skills	• Measuring height and weight • Recording blood pressure measurements • Understanding test results
Communication skills	• Using appropriate language • Using appropriate vocabulary • Demonstrating good listening skills
Personal skills or attributes	• Being **empathetic**, approachable, caring, organised, reliable, helpful, calm, compassionate and non-judgemental
Professional attributes	• Carrying out duties and responsibilities correctly • Following policies and procedures • Being responsible and reliable
Digital skills	• Inputting notes, records and reports • Using monitoring systems • Finding information
Team working and problem-solving skills	• Working with other services and organisations • Working as part of a team and supporting others in the team • Ability to **prioritise** workload • Demonstrating problem-solving skills • Working with other practitioners and valuing their contributions
Learning and reflection skills	• Accepting and acting on feedback • Asking for help or advice when needed • Not being afraid to admit making a mistake
Promote equality and diversity	• Understanding and accepting that people have different views, attitudes, needs and priorities • Treating all individuals fairly and with respect

Five things to know

Working in the health and social care sector

1. General competency skills are very important for health and social care practitioners and care workers.
2. Team-working skills are essential for all health and social care job roles.
3. Being caring, approachable and helpful are important personal attributes for care workers.
4. Care workers are always learning, so being able to reflect on what you have done is important to enable you to improve.
5. People have different needs and should all be treated with respect, whether or not you agree with their views and opinions.

As well as general **competency** requirements, job roles within health and social care services also require specialist skills and qualifications; these vary depending on the type of care being provided.

Social worker

Social workers are usually statutory care workers employed by the local authority. They help their clients find solutions to their problems. An important part of their work is to build a good relationship with the client so that they can work together to make changes to improve the client's situation.

Social workers support many different types of individuals, including:

- older people
- those with learning disabilities, physical disabilities and mental health conditions such as depression, anxiety, schizophrenia and personality disorders
- families at risk of breaking down
- foster carers and adopters
- children who are at risk of abuse or neglect.

Specialist care functions for a social worker

- Visiting clients, who may be in a hospital, care home, hostel or prison.
- Assessing clients' needs and finding out what type of care and support the individual requires.
- Writing and reviewing care plans.
- Listening to individuals, talking with a wide range of people, explaining care plans, using appropriate vocabulary.
- Taking action when individuals are in need support or **safeguarding**.
- Organising support, such as domiciliary care or counselling.
- Making referrals to other services, such as occupational therapy.
- Keeping detailed and accurate records, writing reports and undertaking risk assessments.
- Attending meetings and case conferences.
- Working and communicating with others, such as the police, schools and health services.

Qualifications and experience

Some of the following are essential to become a social worker, while others are desirable.

- A university degree in social work.
- Ideally some work experience, for example a work placement or volunteering.
- Experience gained on a social care apprenticeship will be useful.
- Relevant personal experience may be helpful, such as being a carer.

My life as a social worker

Use the link below to read a case study about a social worker.

www.skillsforcare.org.uk/Documents/Careers-in-care/Case-studies/JaneHaywood.pdf

Jargon buster

Competency – having the ability or skills to do something correctly.

Empathetic – having an understanding of other people's feelings.

Prioritise – deciding the order for dealing with several tasks according to their importance.

Safeguarding – actions taken to protect individuals by reducing the risks of danger, harm and abuse.

Nurse

Nurses perform a wide range of clinical and health care tasks in many different types of settings such as hospitals, nursing homes, GP surgeries and in the community, depending on the type of nursing care they specialise in. Some examples of different types of nurse include:

- general nurse on a hospital ward
- intensive care nurse
- midwife
- school nurse
- community psychiatric nurse
- elderly care nurse
- GP practice nurse
- **health visitor**
- **district nurse**
- mental health nurse
- children's nurse.

Specialist care functions for a nurse

- Carrying out a range of clinical tasks such as taking blood samples, changing wound dressings, monitoring blood pressure and temperature.
- Carrying out health care tasks such as monitoring food and fluid intake.
- Administering medication.
- Recording medical information on patient records.

Qualifications and experience

To become a nurse, you will need:

- a university degree in nursing
- to be registered with the Nursing and Midwifery Council (NMC).

Further training is needed in order to become a midwife or health visitor.

Jargon buster

District nurse – supports the general needs of the local community, providing care at home. This may include caring for someone discharged from hospital, or an older person who could be recovering from a fall, for example. They also have additional training in public health, which enables them to support good health and prevent illness within the community.

Health visitor – a qualified and registered nurse who works in the community to monitor the development of babies and children.

Check what you know

Describe four general skills and four specialist skills needed to be a nurse.

Doctor

Doctors are highly-qualified medical practitioners who examine patients, diagnose illness and disease, and prescribe and carry out treatment. They may be hospital based or work in the community. The work is very varied and as well as treating patients, may include:

- leading a team of medical staff
- managing a department
- teaching and supervising trainee doctors
- carrying out ward rounds/patient clinics
- writing reports and keeping others informed about the diagnosis, care and treatment of their patients as appropriate.

Specialist care functions for a doctor

There are many different areas that doctors can specialise in:

- **Surgery** – caring for patients before, during and after an operation.
- **Anaesthesia** – preparing patients for surgery, giving anaesthetics to patients, monitoring patients during surgery and stabilising patients in the accident and emergency department.
- **Medicine** – treating general medical conditions and specialising in areas such as cardiology (dealing with disorders of the heart), geriatrics (older people), gynaecology or obstetrics (female reproductive system and childbirth).
- **Paediatrics** – caring for the health of babies, children and young people.
- **Psychiatry** – working with individuals who have mental health conditions.
- **General practice** – working as a GP in the local community.

Qualifications and experience

To become a doctor, you will need:

- a five-year degree in medicine
- two-year programme of general training
- specialist training lasting between four and six years, depending on the specialism.

Health care assistant

Health care assistants help with the day-to-day care of patients in hospitals, care homes and nursing homes or in their own homes. They work under the guidance of a qualified health care professional. They need the ability to relate to people of all ages from a wide range of backgrounds, and good written and spoken communication skills.

Specialist care functions for a health care assistant

- Personal care – helping patients shower and get dressed.
- Helping and supporting individuals to eat.
- Making beds.
- Using equipment such as hoists to lift and move patients.
- Helping patients to the toilet.
- Tidying the hospital ward or patients' homes.
- Attending meetings with other health care professionals.
- With additional training, some health care assistants can change wound dressings and carry out some vaccinations.

Qualifications and experience

There are no set requirements to become a health care assistant but employers may ask for:

- GCSEs at grades 9–4 (A*–C) in English and maths
- a qualification in health and social care
- some paid or voluntary experience in health or social care.

My life as a health care assistant

I help lots of different health care professionals with their daily tasks: everyone from nurses, doctors and health care assistants to porters, housekeepers, physiotherapists and occupational therapists. I've worked in many different departments and wards around the hospital – for example medical, haematology, gastroenterology, surgical, orthopaedics, palliative care, and community and day case departments – which means I've cared for many different types of patients.

The thing I enjoy most is providing individual patient care. Having a direct influence on a person's health is very fulfilling and I love watching a person progress and improve from admission to discharge.

Source: Luke Watson, Queen Elizabeth Hospital, Gateshead
(Health Careers, Health Education England, www.healthcareers.nhs.uk)

Activities co-ordinator

The role of an activities co-ordinator is to organise social activities for people who need care and support, and to assist and encourage them to take part. Figure 1.2 shows a yoga class for older adults. An activities co-ordinator may work in various settings, for example with groups of individuals in residential care homes and day centres. They can also work in individuals' homes or in the community.

Figure 1.2 Taking part in activities such as yoga helps older people keep flexible and mobile

Specialist care functions for an activities co-ordinator

- Discussing with individuals the types of activities they would like to do.
- Organising activities that are tailored to the needs and abilities of individuals.
- Developing group activities that will bring people together to avoid social isolation.
- Planning activities and carrying out risk assessments.
- Organising outings and events.
- Booking external suppliers to provide entertainment.
- Organising trips to the local community, bearing in mind accessibility, transport and health and safety.

Qualifications and experience

To become an activities co-ordinator, you will need:

- an ability to motivate people, and good planning and organisational skills
- no specific qualifications although GCSEs in English and maths may be preferred
- ideally a Level 2 or 3 qualification in health and social care
- work experience in a similar role or volunteering experience
- ideally experience gained on a social care apprenticeship.

Outreach worker

Outreach workers focus on providing support for individuals in the form of advice and guidance, for example for drug or alcohol dependency. They may work for or with drug and alcohol action groups, youth offending services, local authorities and charitable organisations. Outreach work involves finding out about an individual's situation and needs, then talking about their options for support. It may involve going out with police patrols, helping with needle exchange services and running workshops in schools and youth centres to raise awareness.

Specialist care functions for an outreach worker

- Building relationships with community organisations such as tenants' and residents' groups.
- Giving face-to-face advice about health protection.
- Helping individuals get access to housing or benefits and rehabilitation programmes.
- Finding and agreeing the best services to help individuals.
- Working with families to help give the individual wider practical and emotional support.

Qualifications and experience

- There are no set requirements to become an outreach worker but a good understanding of the issues facing individuals with substance misuse problems will be useful.
- Some roles require GCSE English and maths, while others may require a qualification in nursing, counselling or youth work.
- Volunteering for a drug, alcohol or housing charity is a good way to gain relevant experience.

Check what you know

Write a paragraph describing the attributes and skills required for an outreach worker.

Occupational therapist

Occupational therapists work with individuals to support them with independent skills for everyday tasks.

An occupational therapist will help clients find ways to continue with activities that are important to them. This might mean learning new ways to do things or making changes to their home or work environment to maintain independence.

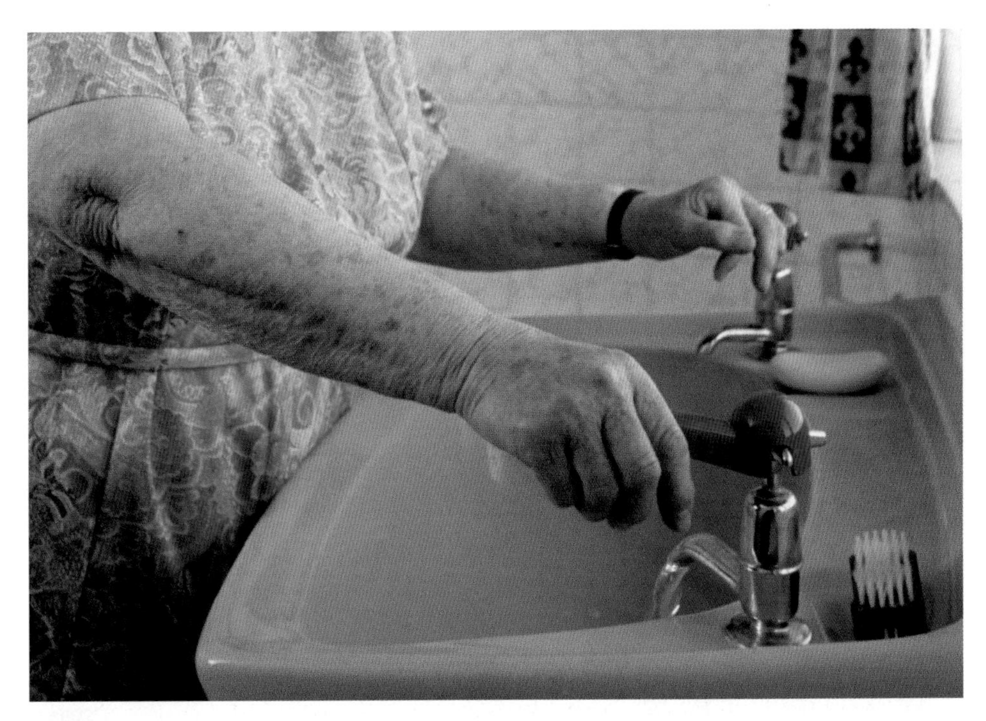

Figure 1.3 An occupational therapist can arrange the supply of specialist aids such as this 'tap turner' to help individuals with a weak grip. The handle makes it easier to hold and use the tap

Specialist care functions for an occupational therapist

- Helping people adjust to their disability.
- Supplying appropriate specialist equipment to help with mobility and fall prevention or items such as kettle tippers and tap turners (see Figure 1.3).
- Supporting clients to adapt their home or car to improve accessibility.
- Helping clients to cope with memory or sensory (vision, hearing) loss.
- Teaching a client who has had a stroke how to do things for themselves again.
- Advising local authority housing departments on mobility issues.
- Providing training for activities co-ordinators.

Qualifications and experience

To become an occupational therapist, you will need:

- a university degree in occupational therapy
- experience gained on an apprenticeship will be useful.

It is possible to begin by working as an occupational therapy support worker, which does not necessarily require any formal qualifications.

Find out more

Occupational therapy

Use the link below to watch a clip of an NHS occupational therapist explaining what her job involves.

www.nhs.uk/video/Pages/Occupationaltherapy.aspx

Counsellor

Counsellors work for the NHS, the local authority, community care or charity organisations. They may also work for a private business that charges for their services. Counselling is a talking therapy that involves a trained therapist listening to an individual to help them to find ways to deal with emotional issues. Counselling allows an individual to talk about their problems and feelings in a safe and supportive environment.

Figure 1.4 A counsellor provides emotional support

Counsellors help individuals to cope with difficult times in their lives and to overcome challenges as well as how to deal with negative thoughts and feelings. For example, they may help individuals who are experiencing anxiety, an eating disorder, gambling, smoking, drug or alcohol addiction or who are coping with major life events such as a long-term illness, bereavement or a relationship breakdown. Counsellors work with individuals and with couples, families or groups. Usually counselling sessions are face-to-face, but they can be by phone, email or via live chat services on the internet. Charities that offer counselling include Cruse (bereavement care), Relate (relationship advice and counselling) and the Samaritans.

Specialist care functions for a counsellor

- Excellent listening skills.
- Provide time and attention to help individuals explore their feelings.
- Ability to encourage individuals to reflect on their experiences.
- Enable people to cope with their challenges.
- Help individuals make positive changes in their lives.

Qualifications and experience

This depends on the level of counselling expertise required.

- A university psychology degree is required to become a counselling psychologist.
- Introductory courses for counselling are available.

Find out more

Social care job roles

Go to the Skills for Care website to find out more in-depth information about different job roles in social care.

www.skillsforcare.org.uk/Careers-in-care/job-roles/Job-roles-in-social-care.aspx

Dietician

Dieticians are health professionals specialising in nutrition. They need a good understanding of science. They usually work in the NHS but can also work in sports nutrition, the food industry and health promotion. Dieticians educate individuals about nutrition, enabling them to make informed and practical decisions about their food choices. Dieticians work with a wide range of people including those with diabetes, high cholesterol, food allergies and intolerances, obesity, learning disabilities and those with swallowing difficulties or an eating disorder. They also look after the nutritional needs of individuals being cared for in intensive care units who might be unconscious.

Specialist care functions for a dietician

- Promote good dietary health.
- Give practical advice about how to achieve a healthy diet.
- Provide guidance about special diets.
- Explain how to prevent problems caused by poor diet.
- Prescribe diets for individuals following an assessment.
- Advise other health professionals, care workers and carers how to provide a healthy diet for their service users.

Qualifications and experience

To become a dietician, you will need:

- a university degree in dietetics
- to be registered with the Health and Care Professions Council.

Find out more

Being a dietician

Use the link to watch a clip of Scott, an NHS dietician, explaining what his job role involves.

www.healthcareers.nhs.uk/explore-roles/allied-health-professionals/roles-allied-health-professions/dietitian

Check what you know

Write a list of general attributes and skills required by all health and social care workers.

Five things to know

Job roles in health and social care

1. Some job roles require professional qualifications which can take many years to obtain.
2. There are other job roles that do not require specialist qualifications.
3. There is a wide range of nursing roles.
4. Doctors can specialise in a number of different areas.
5. The specialist care functions for job roles in health and social care will vary depending on the job role.

■ Learning outcome 3: Understand how health and social care services are accessed (P3, P4, M2)

High priority

Make sure you know:

- the four different types of referral to health and social care services
- when, how and why each type of referral would be used
- what is meant by 'barriers to accessing health and social care services'
- examples of barriers to accessing health and social care services.

3.1 Types of referral used to access health and social care services

Service users can gain access to the services they need in different ways. For example, they might decide to make an appointment with their GP, they might be taken to a hospital A&E department by paramedics for emergency treatment or their GP might send them to see a hospital consultant for tests. Whichever method is used, it is called a 'referral'.

Self-referral

Self-referral is when an individual decides to use a service themselves. Examples of when individuals might self-refer include:

- phoning to make an appointment to see their GP or practice nurse because they are not feeling well
- going to a local NHS walk-in medical centre for treatment of a minor injury
- making a dentist appointment for a check-up
- going to the opticians to have their eyesight tested.

Professional referral

This is when a care professional puts an individual in contact with another service or care practitioner. With the exception of individuals attending A&E in an emergency, hospital services and social care services can only be accessed following referral by a professional.

Examples of professional referral include:

- a GP sending a patient to hospital for an X-ray
- a GP making an appointment for an individual to see a hospital consultant for specialist treatment

- a social worker contacting an occupational therapist to help an individual cope with daily living tasks after having had a stroke
- a health visitor referring a family to the social care services team
- a teacher contacting the local authority because they have concerns about a child.

Compulsory referral

The Mental Health Act (2007) and the Children Act (2004) are laws made by parliament that give certain professionals, such as social workers, police and doctors, the authority to take individuals to a place of safety, without the individual's permission, in order to protect them. This type of referral occurs when an individual is at risk of harming themselves or others or, in the case of a child, being at risk of harm from others.

Examples of compulsory referral include:

- a child taken into care by the local authority because they are at risk of neglect or abuse
- an adult with serious mental health problems taken to hospital for assessment and treatment against their will if they are deemed to be at risk of harming themselves or others.

Read and write

1. Go to the Rethink Mental Illness website and read the Mental Health Act factsheet – www.rethink.org/about-us/all-factsheets
2. Write an explanation of compulsory referral using facts from this textbook and the Mental Health Act factsheet.

Third-party referral

Third-party referral is when an individual is put in touch with health or social care services by a friend, relative or neighbour.

Examples of third-party referral include:

- a neighbour contacting the local authority because they are worried about a child living nearby who appears to be neglected
- a friend telling someone about a voluntary group or charity that can advise them about health or social care services they need but were not aware of
- a relative making a GP appointment for an elderly parent who is getting confused and not eating properly.

Check what you know

State the meaning of the four different types of referral used to access health and social care services:

1. Self-referral
2. Professional referral
3. Compulsory referral
4. Third-party referral

Five things to know

Referral

Make sure you know:

1. the definition of the term 'referral'
2. examples of when self-referral would be used
3. why professional referrals are made
4. the meaning of compulsory referral and when it can happen
5. examples of who would make a third-party referral, and why.

3.2 Barriers to accessing health and social care services

A barrier is something that prevents an individual from using a service or having the care or treatment they need. The different types of barriers and some examples of each are explained below.

Communication

Examples of communication barriers:

- Information not available in different formats, for example Braille or large print for those with visual impairments.
- Hearing loop not available for hearing impaired.
- No staff trained in sign language.
- Information not available in different languages; no interpreter available so individual cannot understand information or explain their symptoms.
- Difficulty finding an effective communication method.

Cultural values and beliefs

Examples of barriers due to cultural values and beliefs:

- Individuals might face discrimination due to their disability, race or age because of past experiences.
- Some cultures regard mental illness and learning disabilities as a stigma and so individuals with these conditions are hidden and not taken for treatment or help.

- In some **cultures** women will not accept treatment from a male practitioner or vice versa.
- Jehovah's Witnesses do not accept blood transfusions.

Jargon buster

Culture – influenced by traditions, customs, beliefs or values held.

Cost

Examples of cost barriers:

- Cost of private service might be too high, for example a private dentist if no NHS dentist is available.
- Cost of transport or car parking fees and difficulty in obtaining time off work put people off attending for treatment.
- Low income may affect access.

Location

Examples of location barriers:

- Specialist services may not be available in the individual's area or postcode.
- Individual cannot reach the service because they cannot drive and there is no public transport, or because of rural isolation.

Physical access

Examples of physical access barriers:

- A lack of ramps, lifts or automatic doors makes access difficult for wheelchair users, those with prams and less mobile individuals and elderly people.
- Individuals might be unable to get to the service due to the effects of medication which might prevent driving or use of public transport.

Psychological

Examples of psychological barriers:

- Individuals may not seek treatment because of fear, for example they may be afraid of the dentist or of having an operation.
- Individuals may also be afraid of having their suspicions of a serious illness confirmed by a diagnosis.
- Some people worry about loss of independence, for example an older person may not want to go into residential care as they do not want to be looked after by others.
- People often avoid accessing services because of pride – they may not want to admit they need help.

- A person with mental health problems might not realise they are ill.
- Some people avoid using a service because of stigma – they have a fear of being labelled, for example because of mental health issues or they may be embarrassed about using the service.
- Some individuals lack the confidence or courage to ask for help.

Lack of resources

Examples of barriers due to lack of resources:

- Some specialist services might not be available in the local area.
- There may be a lack of staff or specialists.
- Some drugs and treatments are not available on the NHS.
- An individual may not be able to afford private treatment if NHS treatment is not available.

Time

Examples of time barriers:

- Sometimes a service may only be available during working hours and an individual may not want their employer to know they are ill, so they do not ask for time off for appointments.
- Regular hospital appointments can take up a lot of time, so may prevent attendance by those individuals who are working or who require child care during their appointments.
- An individual with poor mobility may need to be accompanied by a friend or relative, who may not always be available to help.

Check what you know

1. Explain three examples of communication barriers.
2. Other than communication, identify and explain four barriers to accessing health and social care services.

Theory in action

Gennelle is a 65-year-old woman. She lives alone in her own flat. She had a stroke a while ago and now has limited mobility. She uses a walking frame, and her speech is not as clear as it used to be. Gennelle is happy living alone, but isn't able to get out as much as she would like to. The lift in her building is often out of order and she can't manage the stairs. Gennelle's son visits once a month and her daughter takes her shopping once a week. Gennelle spends a lot of time watching television. She feels a bit lonely but doesn't like to ask for help as she likes to be independent.

Explain any barriers that may prevent Gennelle from accessing health and social care she might need.

Five things to know

Barriers to accessing care

Make sure you know:

1 the meaning of the term 'barriers'
2 the impact for individuals of barriers to accessing care
3 the eight types of barriers to accessing health and social care services
4 examples of barriers to physical access
5 examples of all the other types of barriers to accessing health and social care services.

3.3 How barriers to accessing health and social care services may be overcome

Overcoming communication barriers

Ways of overcoming communication barriers include:

- providing leaflets/information in a variety of formats, such as large print and Braille
- having staff available who are trained in **British Sign Language (BSL)** and **Makaton**
- installing a **hearing loop** to assist individuals with hearing impairments
- providing information leaflets in different languages
- offering access to a translator if the service user cannot speak English
- employing staff who speak languages other than English.

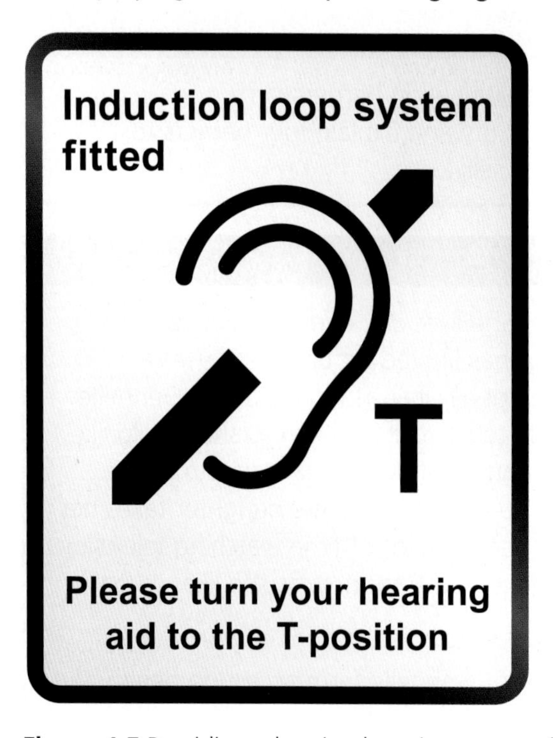

Figure 1.5 Providing a hearing loop is an example of adapting the environment to improve access to health and social care services

Jargon buster

British Sign Language (BSL) – the use of hand movements, gestures, body language and facial expressions to communicate. BSL is used by individuals who are deaf or have a hearing impairment.

Hearing loop – a special type of sound system for use by people with hearing aids. The hearing loop provides a wireless signal that is picked up by the hearing aid and can greatly improve the quality of sound while reducing background noise.

Makaton – the use of speech, gestures and pictures to communicate with individuals who have learning and communication difficulties.

It is important that health and social care practitioners do not create communication barriers themselves. Some ways in which practitioners can use their communication skills effectively are explained below, together with examples of each.

Use vocabulary that can be understood by all:

- Avoid jargon.
- Explain any specialist terminology.
- Use age-appropriate vocabulary.
- Use simplified language, for example with young children, individuals with learning disabilities or patients with dementia.
- Use interpreters or translators.

Use communication that is appropriate to the individual:

- Use positive body language, such as nodding in agreement and making eye contact.
- Avoid sarcasm and do not talk down to the person.
- Be polite.
- Make the service user feel they are being taken seriously.
- Be patient, especially when listening to repetition.
- Do not ignore the person's views or beliefs just because they are different to yours.

Listen to the individual's needs:

- Use active listening by demonstrating interest in response to what an individual is saying and appropriate body language to show a positive reaction.
- Ask the individual rather than assuming you know what they want, need or prefer.
- Concentrate on what the individual is saying as this can encourage them to communicate their needs.

Adapt communication to meet the individual's needs or the situation:

- Emphasise important words.
- Slow the pace of conversation if necessary.
- Increase the tone of voice but do not shout.
- Use repetition where appropriate.
- Use gestures or flash cards/pictures, if appropriate.
- Make use of aids to communication, such as a hearing loop system.
- Use specialist communication methods, such as Braille or signing.
- Use technological aids, such as **Dynavox** or a **Lightwriter**.

Jargon buster

Dynavox – speech-generating software that converts text, pictures and symbols on a screen into speech when touched.

Lightwriter – a text-to-speech device that allows a message to be typed on a keyboard, displayed on a screen and then converted into speech.

Overcoming cultural values and belief barriers

Ways of overcoming barriers due to cultural values and beliefs include:

- organising campaigns to raise awareness and change attitudes
- training staff to have positive attitudes
- ensuring there are appropriate numbers of female and male staff available to meet cultural requirements
- employing a range of staff to reflect the local population
- providing for a range of dietary requirements, for example vegetarian, Halal and Kosher.

Overcoming cost barriers

Ways of overcoming cost barriers include:

- providing people with information and advice about benefits that they may be entitled to
- offering cheap or free car parking for service users
- providing free transport to the care service, such as a minibus that collects from around the local area.

Overcoming location barriers

Ways of overcoming location barriers include:

- providing outreach services, such as home visits or mobile surgeries or clinics
- providing buses that take services to more rural areas or to the elderly and those with mobility problems
- setting up a volunteer driver service to and from the care setting
- using an online prescription order and delivery service.

Figure 1.6 Overcoming location and physical barriers to access health and social care services

Overcoming physical access barriers

Ways of overcoming physical access barriers include:

- ensuring all areas of the care setting are accessible and make adaptions if needed, for example by providing ramps, wider doorways, lower height reception desk
- providing disabled car parking spaces
- providing adapted toilets for wheelchair users
- ensuring Braille is shown on lift control panels or have 'talking instructions'.

Overcoming psychological barriers

Ways of overcoming psychological barriers include:

- providing counselling
- providing more information to reduce anxiety
- holding open days to reduce fear of the unknown
- having information campaigns/leaflets so that people know what to expect.

Overcoming resources barriers

Local clinical commissioning groups will assess the needs of individuals in the area to ensure that the services required by the community are available. For example, an area that has many young families will need children and young people's services, whereas an area with a mainly ageing population will need resources to be put into residential care, day centres and homecare services.

The **National Institute for Health and Care Excellence (NICE)** is a government organisation that decides whether new treatments and drugs should be available on the NHS. Approval of new drugs and treatments can remove barriers for some individuals who currently cannot be treated because the drugs they require are not yet available on the NHS and are too expensive for them to buy themselves.

Charity organisations provide many services to supplement those available from the NHS and local authority social care providers.

Jargon buster

National Institute for Health and Care Excellence (NICE) – assesses new drugs and treatments to establish their effectiveness for patients and whether they are cost effective for supply by the NHS. Drugs and treatments are only available on the NHS if they have been approved by NICE.

Overcoming time barriers

Ways of overcoming time barriers include:

- extending opening hours of GP surgeries, clinics, etc.
- offering flexible appointment times to suit individual needs
- using technology for appointments, such as Skype, video-calling or telephone appointments.

Check what you know

Identify and explain a possible barrier to accessing care for each of the following individuals:

1. An 87-year-old man who has a hospital appointment
2. A 7-year-old girl who has toothache
3. A woman who needs specialist breast cancer treatment
4. An individual who needs to see their GP after work
5. A man who is a wheelchair user

Activity

To help you remember all the types of barriers to accessing health and social care and how they can be overcome, create a mind map with the word 'Barriers' in the centre.

Add sections for each type of barrier – 'Physical', 'Communication', 'Location', etc.

Beneath each of these headings, add in as many ways as you can think of to overcome the barriers.

Learning outcome 4: Understand specific care needs and services accessed by individuals throughout the life stages (P5, M3)

High priority

Make sure you know:

- the six life stages
- that individuals need care at all stages of life
- examples of care needs at each life stage
- examples of health and social care services accessed at each life stage.

4.1 Care needs of individuals through the life stages

Accidents and short- or long-term illness can occur at any life stage and will result in specific care needs. However, groups of people at the same life stage, for example infancy, adolescence or later adulthood, will generally have similar care needs.

Infancy (0–2 years)

Babies and infants are unable to meet their own care needs. They are dependent on their carers for everything they require for **growth** and **development**. Figure 1.7 shows the care needs in infancy.

Jargon buster

Development – the process of learning skills, e.g. movement, language, thinking, feelings.

Growth – a physical increase in size.

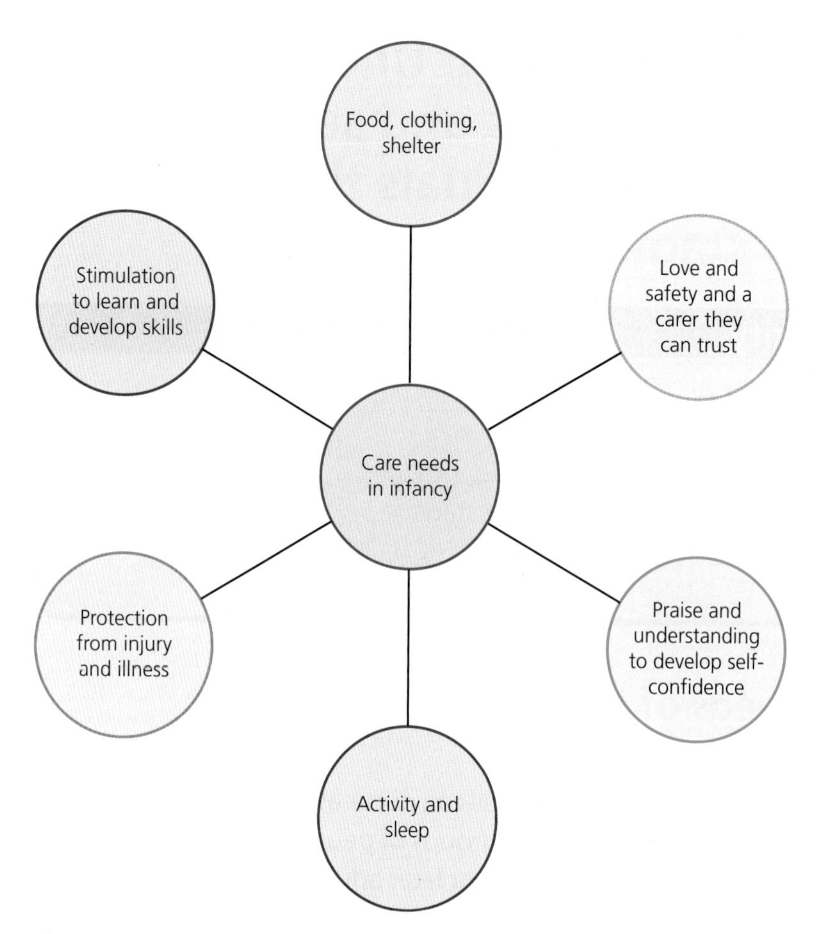

Figure 1.7 Care needs in infancy

Childhood (3–10 years)

Throughout this life stage, children gradually become less dependent on their carers and begin to develop new interests and learn skills such as walking, riding a tricycle and making friends. They are, however, still dependent on others to look after them.

Care needs for children include:

- health – immunisations, personal hygiene, nutrition and a balanced diet
- exercise
- rest and sleep
- opportunities to play and learn
- opportunities to develop social skills.

Activity

In pairs or small groups, discuss possible care needs of adolescents. Consider the following:

- health needs
- social needs
- emotional needs.

Early adulthood (18–29 years)

During this life stage adults are likely to be able to take control of their own lives and make their own decisions, but there will also be situations when individuals need help and support.

Possible care needs in early adulthood include:

- contraception/pregnancy
- emotional needs – relating to relationships and work as well as personal social problems
- possible injury such as broken bones
- drug and alcohol problems
- dietary intolerances may develop, for example **coeliac disease** or **IBS**
- unexpected illnesses or accidents affecting physical or mental health.

Jargon buster

Coeliac disease – a disease in which the body's immune system mistakes substances such as gluten in food as a threat and attacks them, leading to symptoms that can cause severe discomfort.

IBS (irritable bowel syndrome) – a disorder where food moves through the digestive system too quickly or too slowly, causing cramps, bloating and other symptoms.

Middle adulthood (30–60 years)

This can be a period of pressure and stress as a result of family and work responsibilities leading to physical, emotional and social care needs. Individuals may be caring for older parents as well as their own family, they may become unemployed or be trying to juggle family life with the demands of work.

Possible care needs in middle adulthood include:

- pregnancy
- menopause causing physical and physiological changes
- coping with stress due to work, redundancy, unemployment or family responsibilities
- emotional needs due to, for example, relationship breakdowns, family responsibilities or **bereavement**
- development of illnesses such as diabetes, heart disease, **arthritis** or cancer.

Jargon buster

Arthritis – a condition that causes pain, swelling and inflammation in the joints.

Bereavement – the period following the loss of a loved one, such as a friend, partner, wife, husband, parent or child.

Late adulthood (60+ years)

Not all older individuals are frail and unwell. However, all people are affected in some way by the ageing process, though some may experience the effects earlier than others.

Care needs in late adulthood include:

- **chronic** health problems, such as heart disease, arthritis, **osteoporosis**, Alzheimer's disease or cancer
- sensory problems – vision and hearing may start to decline
- loss of mobility – resulting in a need for care and support in the home
- emotional needs as a result of social isolation due to loneliness or a person feeling they are a nuisance or burden for their family to look after.

Jargon buster

Chronic – refers to an illness or condition that lasts longer than three months and that is ongoing; the illness can be controlled but not cured.

Osteoporosis – a loss of bone density which leads to weakened bones that fracture easily.

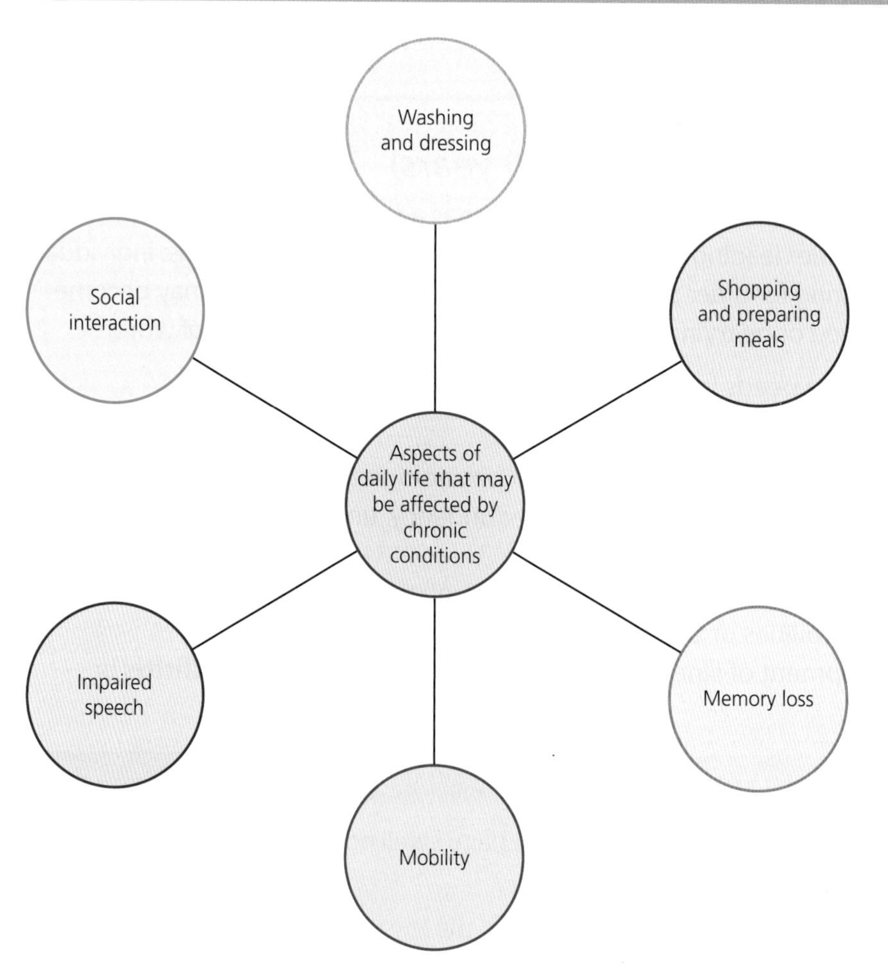

Figure 1.8 Aspects of daily life affected by long-term illness

Five things to know

Care needs and life stages

Make sure you know:

1. the names of the six different life stages
2. a brief description of each life stage
3. care needs that all infants will have
4. unexpected care needs that could occur at any life stage
5. care needs created by a long-term illness.

Activity

List examples of care needs for each life stage.

4.2 Health and social care services accessed by individuals through the life stages

Individuals use health and social care services throughout their lives. They access support from these care services at different times and for different lengths of time, depending on their specific needs and the type of illness or condition they have.

Health care services

A wide range of health care services are provided throughout the life stages, as described below.

- **Maternity services** – provided by midwives, GPs and hospitals – this includes routine tests during pregnancy, identifying concerns, providing information about labour, advice about diet and lifestyle and well baby clinics.
- **Children's care** – provided by GPs, health visitors and hospitals – includes childhood developmental screening, immunisations, treating childhood illness and specialist medical care.
- **General health care** – provided by GPs who treat routine illnesses, prescribe medication and make referrals to other services for specialised tests or care.
- **Medical care for all ages** – provided by specialised hospital doctors, including surgery, tests, medical screening and scans.
- **Nursing care for babies, children and adults** – provided in hospital and nursing homes or provided in the community by midwives, health visitors and district nurses.
- **Mental health care services** – counselling, psychological therapy, rehabilitation and psychiatric care are provided for all life stages.
- **Dental, eyesight and hearing services** – screening, monitoring and treatment are provided for all life stages.

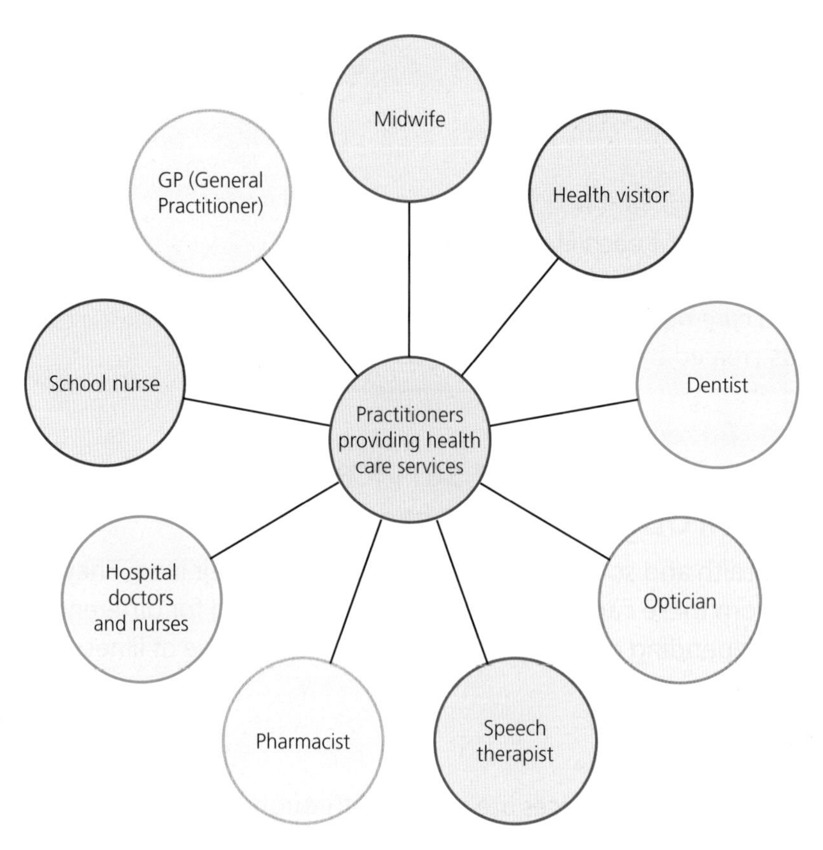

Figure 1.9 Practitioners who provide health care services for infants, children and adults

Theory in action

Figure 1.10 George

→

George is 86 years old and accesses a number of health care services:

- **GP** – the doctor examines George, writes a prescription for painkillers and refers him to the hospital to see a doctor who specialises in bones and joints (an orthopaedic doctor).
- **Hospital** – George sees the orthopaedic doctor who arranges X-rays, examines him and then diagnoses arthritis in George's finger and wrist joints. George is told to keep taking the painkillers and to return to his GP if they do not help. The doctor refers George to a podiatrist (foot doctor), a physiotherapist and an occupational therapist.
- **Podiatrist** – George has his corns and hard skin removed and his toe nails are trimmed. This should help to stop his feet hurting.
- **Physiotherapist** – George is taught some simple exercises to help strengthen his muscles and maintain his mobility. The exercises will make it easier for George to grasp objects and move around more easily.
- **Occupational therapy** – the occupational therapist carries out an assessment of the problems George is having with using his hands. He arranges to supply George with some specialist aids to help with everyday tasks, including a tap turner and a kettle pourer to help him make a cup of tea more easily.
- **Optician** – George makes himself an appointment with his optician. The optician thoroughly checks George's eyesight and he is told there are no serious problems. He is prescribed a stronger pair of glasses so that he can read his newspaper once again.
- **Dentist** – George makes an appointment to see his dentist. His teeth and gums are checked and his teeth are cleaned. George is advised he needs to have two teeth removed and a dental bridge fitted to replace them. The dentist tells George he will be able to chew properly again when this dental work is done.

Questions

1. What is George's life stage?
2. What type of referral is used by George's GP?
3. What type of referral is used to arrange appointments with the optician and dentist?
4. Explain three examples of barriers that could stop George from accessing services.
5. Describe how the barriers you suggested could be overcome.

Check what you know

Write down three places that a new mother could go to for health advice about her baby.

My life as a health visitor

I have been a health visitor for 13 years. This is a typical day:

9 a.m.	Administration and phone calls that have come in overnight, including: • parents looking for advice • messages from social workers with concerns about families • call from the hospital about a baby that is ready to be discharged home • information about a baby that has been born early.
9.15 a.m.	New birth visit, which usually lasts about two hours, to a family who have just had their first baby. I assess the baby physically, find out how he is feeding and give support and advice with breastfeeding if needed. I also assess the parents' mood, checking for signs of postnatal depression in both mum and dad. I provide them with information about support available in the local area such as children's centres and baby clinics.
11.30 a.m.	Antenatal visit to a vulnerable mother-to-be who has a history of anxiety and depression. The focus of our discussion is developing positive mental health and awareness of support that is available locally.
12.30 p.m.	Weekly team meeting which includes the allocation of visits regarding ten-month and two-year developmental checks, families where safeguarding is an issue and planning baby clinic cover. We also discuss the allocation of families referred to us by GPs, police, social workers and local hospitals.
2 p.m.	Meeting with Children's Social Care Service regarding a family with two children, both on a child protection plan. The team includes a lead social worker, myself, a mental health support worker and a drug/alcohol support worker. The mother attends the meeting with her baby, while her other child is at pre-school. The protection plan is discussed and agreed with the mother to ensure she is fully involved.
3.30–5 p.m.	Record keeping is an important part of the job, so I return to the office in time to input the details of today's visits into the electronic record system.

Social care services

A wide range of social care services are provided, as outlined below.

- Children and their families may use early education services with support from practitioners such as primary teachers, nursery staff and childminders.
- Fostering and adoption services will be involved when a child is placed in short-term foster care while their carer recovers from an illness or surgery and is unable to look after them; when a child is taken into care to protect them from abuse or a chaotic home life; when individuals decide to foster or adopt a child.
- Domiciliary care may be provided temporarily if an adult is recovering from surgery for example, or can be put in place long term for an older adult who can no longer manage daily living tasks on their own.
- A social worker may provide support for an adolescent or young adult who is leaving care and moving into employment, providing advice and guidance about independent living.
- An outreach worker could provide support for adolescents or adults with drug addiction issues.
- Alcohol support services are provided by local authorities for adolescents and adults, as well as by self-help groups such as Alcoholics Anonymous and other, local support groups; there is also a national helpline provided by Drinkline.
- Social workers and family support workers may support a mother and her children in situations involving domestic abuse, by providing temporary housing for example.
- Older adults and individuals who have a physical or learning disability may access support from community services and day centres.
- Bereavement counselling can be provided for individuals who have lost a partner, parent or other close family member or friend.
- Support groups such as Macmillan Cancer Support or Arthritis Action for adults, adolescents and children who have, or are caring for, individuals – see Table 1.5 (page 45) for further examples.

Figure 1.1 (page 5) shows a range of different types of health and social care services available to support children and families.

Find out more

Health and social care services used during the middle adulthood life stage

Interview someone who is over 50 and who has had children. Ask them about the health and social care services they have used between the ages of 30 and 50.

My life as a social worker

My name is Tom and I am a social worker, mainly working with families. Being a social worker is often a challenging yet rewarding career. Social workers are responsible for helping individuals, families and groups of people in order to improve outcomes.

I never know what each day will bring: a typical day can range from making an unannounced home visit to check if a client's violent My name is Tom and I am a social worker, mainly working with families. Being a social worker is often a challenging yet rewarding career. Social workers are responsible for helping individuals, families and groups of people to cope with problems they are facing in order to improve their clients' lives.

I never know what each day will bring: a typical day can range from making an unannounced home visit to check if a client's violent ex-husband has moved back in, followed by a meeting to decide how to help parents whose seven-year-old still isn't in school, then on to break the news to a child that their mum has been caught shop-lifting again and we need to arrange foster care for them.

Drug-using parents are the most challenging cases to deal with. It is really difficult when a child opens the door and when you go in and see in the parents' eyes that they are using again, in spite of the drug support work done with them. It is extremely difficult to make the decision to take a child away from their parents and it is made only in extreme cases and by a panel of experts with a judge. But it is a huge relief that we have taken a child out of harm's way.

The best parts of my job are when a family is doing OK, when a child starts attending school for a whole week or when a young person begins to come out of their shell and talks about what is going on in their life.

Figure 1.11 Social workers provide support for families

Read and write

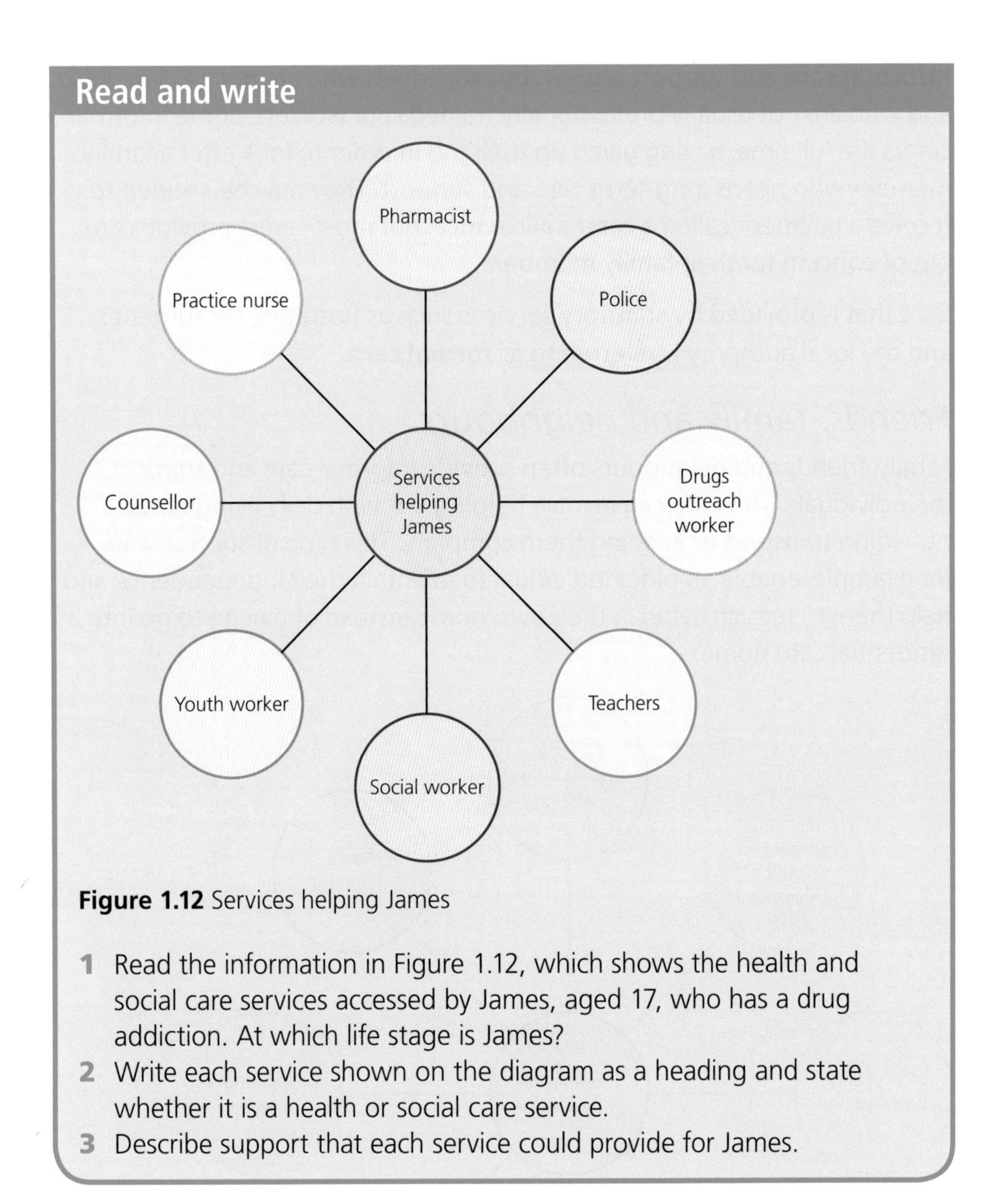

Figure 1.12 Services helping James

1. Read the information in Figure 1.12, which shows the health and social care services accessed by James, aged 17, who has a drug addiction. At which life stage is James?
2. Write each service shown on the diagram as a heading and state whether it is a health or social care service.
3. Describe support that each service could provide for James.

■ Learning outcome 5: Understand informal care (P6, D1)

5.1, 5.2 The role of informal care and types of informal carers

High priority

Make sure you know:

- the meaning of the term 'informal care'
- who provides informal care
- examples of the type of care provided by informal carers.

Jargon buster

Formal care – provided by, for example, statutory services such as a hospital, GP surgery or the local authority. Staff are qualified or trained and are employed to provide their services.

Informal care – provided by individuals who are not paid to do so, such as family, friends, neighbours and volunteers.

Informal care and support is given by individuals who are not paid to do so and who are not usually professionally trained care workers. Some informal carers are full time, having given up their job in order to look after a family member who needs long-term care and support. They may be entitled to receive a payment called a carer's allowance, but most carers provide care out of concern for their family member.

Care that is provided by statutory services such as hospitals, GP surgeries and the local authority is referred to as **formal care**.

Friends, family and neighbours

Family, friends and neighbours often provide informal care and support for individuals. This care can involve helping out with daily living tasks, providing transport or keeping them company. This type of support can, for example, enable an older individual to maintain their independence and help them to remain living in their own home instead of having to go into a residential care home.

Extend

Access the website of an organisation that provides support groups, such as Macmillan Cancer Support, and describe all of the different types of support it can provide for individuals and their families.

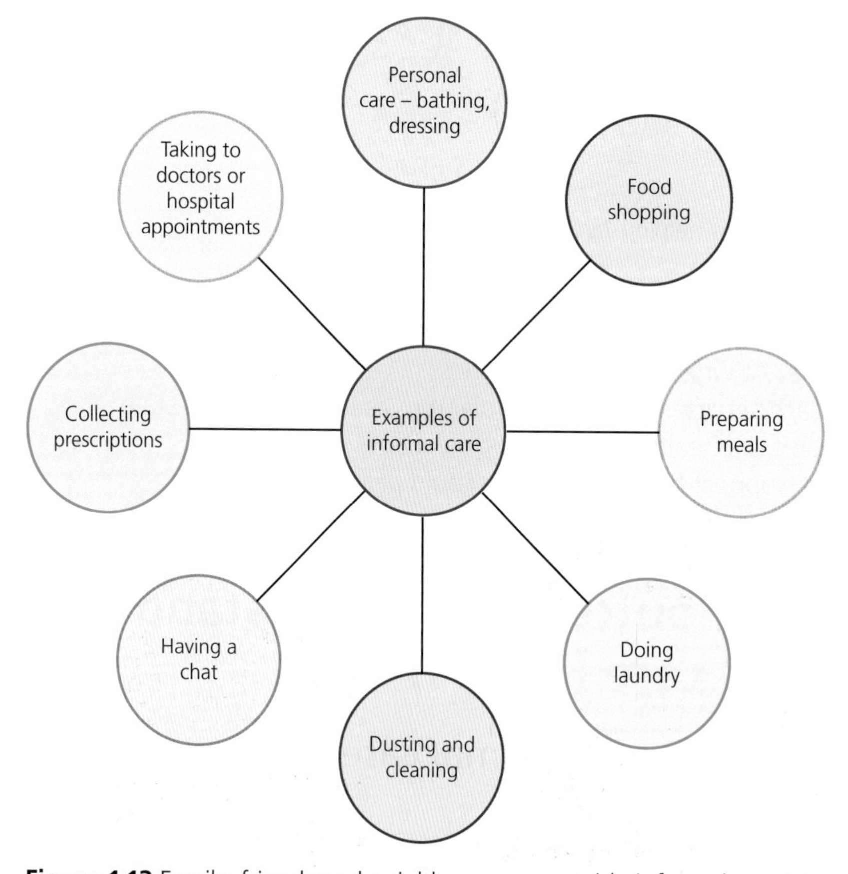

Figure 1.13 Family, friends and neighbours can provide informal care

Community groups

Some informal carers form local community groups such as 'self-help' groups that meet regularly. These groups give people the chance to talk with others who understand what they are going through while caring for a family member, because they have experienced it themselves.

Charities and support organisations such as Age UK, MIND and Macmillan Cancer Support set up groups in local communities where people with common experiences or concerns can meet and provide each other with information, advice, encouragement and coping strategies.

Volunteers

Volunteers are unpaid and provide support for individuals who have a particular need. People who volunteer are trained by the charitable organisation to provide support. Table 1.5 describes some examples of organisations that provide volunteers to support individuals in the community.

Table 1.5 Organisations providing voluntary care

Organisation	Examples of care provided by volunteers
Age UK	Provide a volunteer to help an older person to fill in complicated benefits claim forms.
Empower Me	Provide a volunteer advocate to write a letter or attend appointments and meetings etc., on behalf of an individual with a learning disability.
Mencap	Provide volunteers who work with individuals of all ages who have learning disabilities.
Royal Voluntary Service	Provide volunteers who visit older people in hospital and help them settle back at home after a hospital stay; they can do shopping and run lunch clubs.
Salvation Army	This is a faith-based organisation that provides homeless people with somewhere to sleep, a meal and hot drinks.
Samaritans	Provide a telephone helpline service for individuals feeling desperate and experiencing distress or contemplating suicide.

Check what you know

Name an organisation that is a provider of voluntary care. What types of care do they provide?

Extend

1. Identify one formal care provider and one informal care provider.
2. Compare and contrast the two care providers by writing a list of their similarities and differences.

Learning outcome 6: Understand regulation and inspection in health and social care provision (P7, D2)

High priority

Make sure you know:

- the meaning of the terms '**regulator**' and '**inspection**'
- the roles of the **Care Quality Commission (CQC)** and **Ofsted**
- the impact (effects) of regulatory inspection on individuals using care services and on the service providers
- the impact of regulatory inspection on how the public judges care providers.

Jargon buster

Care Quality Commission (CQC) – a government organisation responsible for checking standards in health and social care settings.

Inspection – the process of carrying out checks to see whether services provided meet the required standards.

Ofsted – the government organisation that inspects social care services that care for children and young people and also any services providing education and skills training for learners of all ages.

Regulator – an independent organisation that carries out inspections to monitor and rate the quality of services provided.

6.1 The role of regulatory and inspection bodies

Health and social care services are regulated by official government organisations. The regulations (rules) are set in law and state the standards that have to be met by care settings. Inspections are carried out by the regulators, for example the CQC and Ofsted, to see whether services are safe, effective and well-managed, and whether they meet the needs of their service users.

As a result of an inspection, care settings may have to make improvements to their services in order to continue providing care. Regulations and inspections enable service users to be informed about the quality and standard of care that is being provided and to have trust in the services they use.

Care Quality Commission (CQC)

The CQC is the regulator of health and social care for England. It carries out inspections of care services such as hospitals, GP surgeries, care homes, community care services, mental health services and social service departments to ensure that care standards are being met.

The role of the CQC includes:

- registering care services to ensure fundamental standards of quality and safety are met
- carrying out inspections of health and social care settings to monitor that the care provided continues to meet the standards required
- publishing inspection reports which rate care settings (see Figure 1.14)
- issuing cautions, warning notices and fines if standards are not met
- putting a care provider into special measures – this means informing them of improvements which have to be made within a specified time limit and re-inspection within six months.

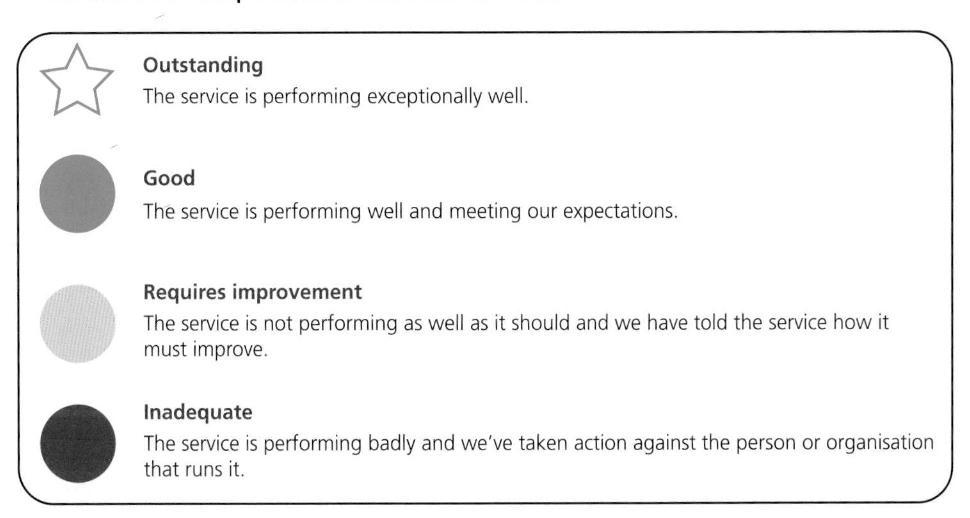

Figure 1.14 Care Quality Commission inspection ratings (source: Care Quality Commission, www.cqc.org.uk)

Theory in action

Go to the CQC website using the link: www.cqc.org.uk/search/services/care-homes

Under the heading 'Overall rating', choose 'Requires improvement'. This will bring up a list of care homes in that category.

Choose a care home, then click on the link 'Read overall summary' and read the summary before answering the questions below.

Questions

1. State two examples of poor practice identified in the CQC report.
2. State two examples of good practice identified in the CQC report.
3. Explain how the inspection report findings will help the service provider to improve their standard of care.

Check what you know

State four ways that the CQC makes sure that care provided by a care service is of the correct standard.

Ofsted

Ofsted (Office for Standards in Education) is a government organisation that inspects and regulates social care services that care for children and young people, as well as those services that provide education and skills training, such as schools and colleges.

Aspects of service provision inspected include:

- effectiveness of leadership and management
- quality of teaching, learning and assessment
- personal development, behaviour and welfare
- outcomes for children and learners
- effectiveness of safeguarding.

Source: The common inspection framework: education, skills and early years

Following an inspection, the setting is given one of the following ratings: 'outstanding', 'good', 'requires improvement' or 'inadequate'.

The inspection report will identify good practice that the inspectors observed and indicate what needs to be improved. These areas for improvement will be checked again at the next inspection with the expectation that the issues have been dealt with and improvements made. Ofsted will put failing settings rated 'inadequate' into special measures which means they will be re-inspected and checked to monitor progress and improvements to the aspects of service that have been identified as unsatisfactory.

The social care common inspection framework (SCCIF) can be accessed here: www.gov.uk/government/collections/social-care-common-inspection-framework-sccif

Check what you know

1. What are the five key aspects of service provision inspected by Ofsted?
2. State how Ofsted checks that a setting makes improvements after being rated as 'inadequate'.

Figure 1.15 Ofsted identifies good practice in services providing education

Impact of regulatory inspection

Impact on individuals accessing services:

- Individuals will be aware of the standards of care they can expect from care settings.
- Regulation and inspection improves the standards of care that individuals receive.
- Individuals are provided with information that enables them to choose a care service with a good rating.
- Individuals know that action is taken if care is not provided to the correct standards.

Impact on the service provider:

- The service will be aware of their responsibilities.
- They will be made aware of weaknesses in the care they provide.
- They may receive a caution, a fine or be taken to court for serious breaches of care regulations.
- The setting may be closed down or de-registered if care continues to be inadequate.
- The strengths of the quality of care provided are identified.
- Inspection helps practitioners do their job effectively, because they know what needs to improve.

Jargon buster

Transparency – not concealed, hidden or covered up; the inspections show things exactly as they are, whether it is good or not.

Impact on public trust:

- There is **transparency** about the standard of services being provided.
- The public know that independent checks are carried out.
- Inspection gives people confidence in the quality of health and social care services.
- The rating grade may help individuals to choose whether or not to use that service.
- The ratings enable individuals to compare services and care settings.

Extend

1 Find an Ofsted report for a setting, such as a childminder or pre-school, which has been graded 'requires improvement'. Use this link: https://reports.ofsted.gov.uk
You can then use the filters to select the type of setting and the rating to narrow down your search.
2 Read the report and make a list of the main strengths of the setting that Ofsted has identified.
3 Read the 'What does the setting need to do to improve further?' section and make a list of the main recommendations.
4 Write an explanation of the impact of the inspection report on:
a) the service provider
b) individuals using the care service.

Check what you know

State one impact of regulatory inspection for each of the following (choose a different impact for each):

1 Individuals using the service
2 The service provider
3 Public trust

Five things to know

Regulation and inspection of services

1 The CQC is the regulator of health and social care for England.
2 Ofsted inspects and regulates social care services that care for children and young people and services providing education and skills training.
3 Inspections will identify good practice and also indicate what needs to be improved.
4 Inspection ratings enable individuals to compare services and care settings.
5 Care settings may receive a caution, a fine or be taken to court and closed down, or de-registered if care continues to be inadequate.

Professional practice and the health and social care practitioner

About this unit

This unit gives you the opportunity to explore working practice in health and social care and how it is underpinned by the care values in order to provide person-centred care. The skills, attributes and behaviours needed by care practitioners and the importance of working within the boundaries of the law are considered. You will learn the main differences between working and personal relationships and how different health and social care practitioners and agencies work together to meet the holistic needs of service users. Different career pathways and how to achieve them by creating a personal development plan are also explored.

Assessment of learning grid

Grade	Learning outcome	Assessment of learning
P1	2	**Identify** current legislation and standards that underpin practice in health and social care. A minimum of two (2) pieces of legislation and one (1) standard must be included.
P2	1	**Describe** four (4) professional skills, behaviours and attributes required by health and social care practitioners.
P3	2	**List** four (4) health and social care values.
P4	1	**Explain** using examples, two (2) reasons why health and social care practitioners must work within the requirements of their given job role.
P5	1 and 4	**Identify** benefits of continuing professional development for: • self and own career development • career pathways and progression in health and social care • individuals accessing health and social care services • health and social care practitioners.
P6	4	**Create** a personal development plan to identify own training and development needs in relation to career development. **Identify** own training and development needs through a personal development plan.
P7	2	**Define** person-centred practice.
P8	3	**Compare** professional and personal relationships for partnership working.
M1	1	**Explain** the impact of professional skills, behaviours and attributes of the health and social care practitioner on an individual accessing a service.
M2	2	**Explain** how person-centred care meets the holistic needs of individuals accessing health and social care services.
M3	3	**Describe** characteristics of partnership working and identify barriers to working effectively with others. A minimum of three (3) barriers must be identified.
D1	2	**Explain** how health and social care values are embedded into the role of the health and social care practitioner. Examples from daily practice must be included. **Use** examples to explain three (3) ways that the health and social care practitioner values individuals accessing services.
D2	3	**Summarise** how partnership working meets the needs of individuals accessing health and social care services.

Learning outcome 1: Understand the responsibilities of health and social care practitioners (P2, P4, P5, M1)

High priority

Make sure you know:

- the professional skills, behaviours and attributes needed by health and social care practitioners
- the impact of professional skills, behaviours and attributes on individuals accessing health and social care services
- the importance of following the requirements of a job description
- the importance of continuing professional development.

1.1 Professional skills, behaviours and attributes required by health and social care practitioners

A professional can carry out their job role in a skilful and knowledgeable way, demonstrating an approach that is appropriate and acceptable for the job role.

For example, some professional **skills** are needed in order to carry out a particular job or task, such as a nurse giving an injection, a surgeon carrying out an operation or a social worker developing a care plan. Professional skills also include the ability to work as part of a team and having effective communication and interpersonal skills. **Behaviours** are about how an individual puts into practice the personal **attributes** they have and reflects the type of person they are: kind, considerate, supportive, organised and efficient, for example.

Jargon buster

Attributes – a quality or a characteristic that someone has, for example confidence, cheerfulness, trustworthiness, a willingness to learn.

Behaviours – the way in which someone acts or conducts themselves in response to a particular situation or person, for example co-operatively, with commitment, calmly.

Skills – having the ability to do specific tasks well.

Theory in action

Look at Figure 2.1 below.

Health care assistant – Person specification		
	Essential	**Desirable**
Academic or vocational qualifications	• Health Studies (or similar) Level 2/3	• A commitment to professional development
Experience	• Experience of working within a nursing team • Experience of dealing with vulnerable patients	
Knowledge and skills	• Blood pressure monitoring • Carrying out new patient medicals • Injections (if trained for specialist care procedures) • Suture/stitch removal • Simple wound care • Testing and processing of specimens • Excellent communication skills	• Experience of smoking cessation clinics • Vascular health checks • Assist with minor surgery procedures
Qualities and attributes	• Ability to work without direct supervision • Can determine own workload priorities • Ability to work as part of a multi-skilled team • Ability to work under pressure • Ability to use own initiative • Confident and outgoing personality	
Other	• Flexibility of working hours to cover colleagues	• Evidence of continuing professional development

Figure 2.1 Person specification for a health care assistant working at a GP surgery

Questions

1. Divide a sheet of paper into three columns headed 'Skills', 'Behaviours' and 'Attributes'.
2. Read the person specification and in the appropriate column list the skills, behaviours and attributes required for a health care assistant.

Examples of skills, attributes and behaviours

The following professional skills, behaviours and attributes are required by health and social care practitioners.

Trustworthy

An individual who is known to be honest, truthful and reliable can be described as trustworthy. It is important that a health and social care practitioner is good and honest and will not harm someone they are caring for. For example, a patient trusts that their GP can be relied on to diagnose an illness correctly and to prescribe appropriate medication or treatment.

Objectivity

Objectivity refers to an absence of bias or prejudice. For example, a social worker's records of an interview with a client should be based on the facts and not influenced by their personal opinions, beliefs or feelings, so that the record is objective. An individual who is objective will value everyone they work with, free from bias or prejudice.

Patience

Patience refers to the ability to wait and accept delays, problems or difficulties without becoming frustrated. For example, a care assistant is patient when handling sensitive issues, allowing individuals to reach decisions they are happy with.

Respect

Respect means taking account of and having regard for someone's feelings, wishes and rights. Showing respect means that when you interact with individuals you value their opinions and treat them with dignity and as an individual. For example, a social worker listening to and taking account of a client's feelings about not wanting to go and live in a residential care home.

Empathy

This refers to the ability to understand and share the feelings of another or understand another person's way of thinking. Showing empathy means imagining what it would be like to be in that person's situation; this can help a care worker to gain a better understanding of others' viewpoints.

Commitment

Commitment means a promise or agreement to do something. It is the responsibility that care workers and practitioners in health and social care services have to those individuals in their care. They commit to perform tasks and carry out the responsibilities of their particular job role to the required standard for the benefit of their service users.

Effective communication and interpersonal skills

Communication is the exchange of information between people, while interpersonal skills are the abilities necessary to interact successfully with other people. Effective use of communication and interpersonal skills will enable individuals who use care services to feel respected, supported and valued and that their needs are being met. Good communication means services users can be actively involved in their care, able to let their changing needs be known and able to make informed choices, as they will have the information needed to develop a clear understanding of procedures, treatments or care plans.

The use of active listening by a care practitioner involves demonstrating an interest in, and responsiveness to, what a person is saying by fully concentrating on what is being said rather than just passively 'hearing'.

It can involve non-verbal cues which show understanding, such as nodding, eye contact and briefly saying 'I see' or 'sure', for example, to build trust and confidence.

Other ways to effectively use communication and interpersonal skills include:

- using vocabulary that can be easily understood – no jargon or specialist medical terminology and age-appropriate explanations
- using specialist methods if needed, such as sign language, a hearing loop, or an interpreter
- adapting communication to meet the needs of individuals by the use of repetition, gestures and body language, flash cards or Braille.

(Also see pages 28–30 in Unit 1, section 3.3 Overcoming communication barriers.)

Figure 2.2 Getting to know an individual

Initiative

Showing initiative means seeing what needs to be done and getting on with it rather than waiting to be told to do it.

Observation skills

This involves watching something or someone in order to gain information. Observation skills are very important in all aspects of health and social care services as they enable care workers to provide a better service for individuals in their care and can also help to make the care environment safer overall.

- Observation is an important aspect of training in health and social care services, and also for the monitoring of care standards in care settings.

- A trainee nurse or doctor will observe a more experienced colleague carrying out surgical procedures so that they can learn how to do it themselves.
- A qualified social worker might observe a trainee leading a care assessment interview, then provide feedback on what went well and provide targets for improvement.
- Trainees in any aspect of health and social care will be observed carrying out tasks to ensure they are doing things correctly and following procedures. Being observed also allows trainees to receive feedback so they know how to improve.
- Good observation skills also benefit service users, by identifying problems early so they can be addressed before they get worse. For example, staff at a children's centre will receive training so they can spot signs of child abuse, neglect or poor treatment.
- Observations such as monitoring an individual's pulse rate, blood pressure or fluid intake are an important part of medical care. The accuracy of such observations is vitally important.
- Observing an individual's reactions when communicating with them can give clues to the way they are feeling, as communication is sometimes through gestures and body language, not just verbal.

Professionalism

Professionalism refers to the ability to carry out a job role in a skilful and knowledgeable way, behaving in a manner that is appropriate and acceptable for that role. When a health and social care professional shows that she can do her job successfully and to a high standard, it enables service users to develop trust and feel confident that they are receiving good quality care and support.

Problem-solving skills

Problem-solving skills are demonstrated when care workers look at a range of solutions to a problem and are able to choose the best way to approach the problem in a logical and reasoned manner.

Teamwork

Teamwork is when a group work together to achieve a common (shared) goal. When working as a part of a team each individual should share information, communicate effectively and work to meet the team's shared goals in the best interests of the service users. Team workers need to be reliable and collaborative.

Teams do not always work together face to face, but they communicate with each other through conference calls, patient records, emails and telephone calls to enable information to be shared.

Examples of team working:

- A GP, midwife, **sonographer**, **obstetrician**, **anaesthetist** and health visitor all work together to achieve the safe development, delivery and postnatal care of a baby.
- A social worker, care assistants, **podiatrist**, GP and occupational therapist work together to enable an 89-year-old woman to remain living at home because she does not want to go into residential care.

Jargon buster

Anaesthetist – a doctor who specialises in pain relief.

Obstetrician – a doctor specialising in the care of pregnant women and who will deliver the baby if there are complications.

Podiatrist – provides foot care such as removing corns and hard skin and ingrowing toe nails.

Sonographer – a health professional who is specially trained to carry out ultrasound scans.

Theory in action

Read the job advertisement in Figure 2.3.

Checkleigh House Children's Centre

Family support worker

Job description
To provide support and advice to families, tailored to their individual needs, within the children's centre and through home visits. You will work as part of the team delivering family support services in the local area.

To apply you need to be:
- Level 3 Health and Social Care qualified or equivalent
- an enthusiastic team worker
- patient and objective
- a good communicator
- a car driver.

Figure 2.3 Job advertisement for a family support worker

Questions

1 Identify the professional skills, behaviours and attributes required for the family support worker job role.
2 Explain the impact, on service users, of the professional skills, behaviours and attributes you identified in question 1.

Activity

1 Choose a job role in health or social care that you are interested in.
2 Write about two key skills, two attributes and two behaviours required for the role.

Reflective practitioner

Being a reflective practitioner means looking back over your work on a regular basis in order to consider and make improvements to your working practices. Reflective practice enables you to know your strengths and weaknesses, identifies ways to improve your work practice and learn new ways of working. Professor Graham Gibbs created a 'reflective cycle' (see Figure 2.4) which provides a structured way for practitioners to analyse and evaluate what they have done and what has happened. Carrying out this review of performance helps the practitioner to identify what could be done better next time.

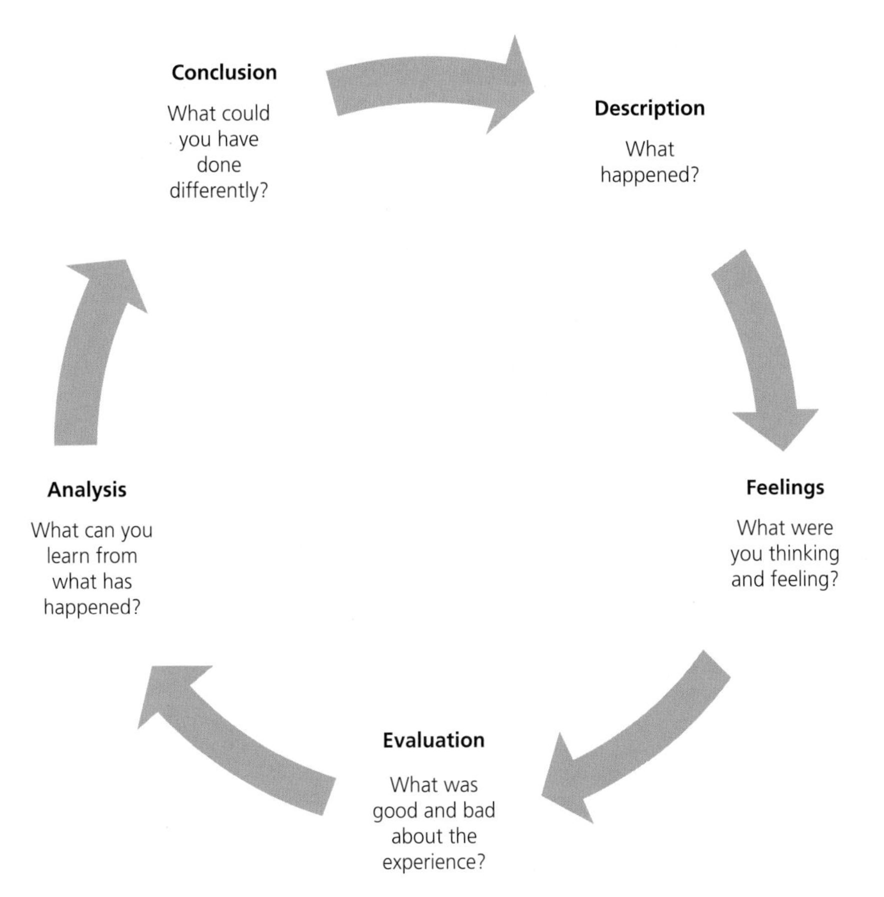

Figure 2.4 Gibbs' reflective cycle

Source: The reflective learning cycle was originally published in Gibbs, G. (1988) *Learning by Doing: A guide to teaching and learning methods*. Further Education Unit. Oxford Polytechnic: Oxford. This book is now available to download as an ebook from the website of the Oxford Centre for Staff and Learning Development, Oxford Brookes University at www.brookes.ac.uk/ocsld/publications

Gibbs' cycle starts with a factual analysis of what has happened and then moves on to encourage the practitioner to consider their thoughts and feelings at the time. This enables an evaluation of strengths and weaknesses of their own performance or of the overall care being provided by the care setting. The practitioner might think: 'Did I do the right thing?', 'Could I have been more helpful to the service user?', 'Do I need more training to improve how I do this?' or 'Can the care setting meet individuals' needs and provide better care in some way?'. Following this analysis, practitioners can identify and plan for their own learning needs or identify ways they or the care setting could improve the quality of care provided.

There are four main aspects a reflective practitioner will consider in order to make improvements to their practice:

- evaluating specific incidents or activities
- exploring their training and development needs
- identifying what might be done better next time to improve
- identifying what went well.

Theory in action

Reflective practice

Jayne is the senior receptionist at a busy hospital outpatients department. A recent patient questionnaire revealed many patients were upset about having limited privacy when discussing personal issues with the receptionists. Jayne decides to investigate the situation and see what can be done to improve the patients' experience, as described in the flow chart in Figure 2.5 below.

Issue

Patients complain that there is limited privacy when discussing personal issues with the receptionists.

↓

Reflective practice

Evaluating specific incidents or activities

Jayne observes staff interactions with patients for two days. She identifies situations when and where patients may be overheard when talking about personal information. While receptionists speak quietly and try to move away from others to maintain confidentiality,it is difficult to achieve this.

Identifying what might be done better next time to improve

An area that provides privacy is needed. Jayne arranges for a little-used storeroom to be emptied, cleaned and decorated. Chairs and a small table are provided so the room can now be used by any staff with patients who need to have a private conversation.

↓

Impact on practice

Patients are routinely asked if they require privacy before discussing anything with them. Receptionists and other staff always use the new room when requested for private conversations with patients to maintain the patient's privacy and confidentiality.

Figure 2.5 Reflective practice in action

Questions

Describe the benefits of Jayne's reflective practice for:

a) staff working in the outpatients department

b) patients attending the outpatients department.

Five things to know

Reflective practice

1. A reflective practitioner is someone who looks back over their work on a regular basis.
2. A reflective practitioner spends time considering, and making, improvements to their working practices.
3. Reflective practice enables a practitioner to know their strengths and weaknesses.
4. A reflective practitioner identifies ways to improve their work practice and learn new ways of working.
5. A reflective practitioner will consider the following aspects in order to make improvements to their practice:
   - evaluating specific incidents or activities
   - exploring their training and development needs
   - identifying what might be done better next time to improve
   - identifying what went well.

1.2 Reasons for health and social care practitioners adhering to their job description

A job description sets out all the responsibilities of a job role and includes detailed information about:

- the tasks, work activities and responsibilities
- how the role is to be carried out
- where the practitioner will work
- who the supervisor or manager is
- hours of work
- how much the practitioner will be paid.

Person specification: Care assistant

Responsibilities and duties

- Assist clients in their homes with personal care tasks, such as washing, dressing, eating and toileting.
- Perform light housekeeping tasks such as dusting, vacuuming and changing bedding.
- Assist in the safe lifting, transferring, repositioning and movement of clients.
- Accompany clients to medical appointments.
- Observe, monitor and record clients' physical and emotional wellbeing and promptly report any changes to senior staff.
- Encourage clients to take part in social and recreational activities.

Skills

- Excellent interpersonal skills
- Level 2 Health and Social Care qualification
- Able to follow policies and procedures and reporting to Care Manager
- First aid trained
- Trained in patient handling and movement is desirable, but training can be provided
- Full time – 38.5 hours per week
- £8.38 – £10.50 per hour

Figure 2.6 Advert for a care assistant

Check what you know

List the key information that is included in a job description.

Read and write

1. Find a job advertisement for a health and social care role you are interested in.
2. Read the information provided then write a detailed job description for that role.

Jargon buster

Adhere – to follow instructions or rules exactly as required.

There are a number of reasons why it is important that practitioners and care workers **adhere** to their job description, as shown in Figure 2.7.

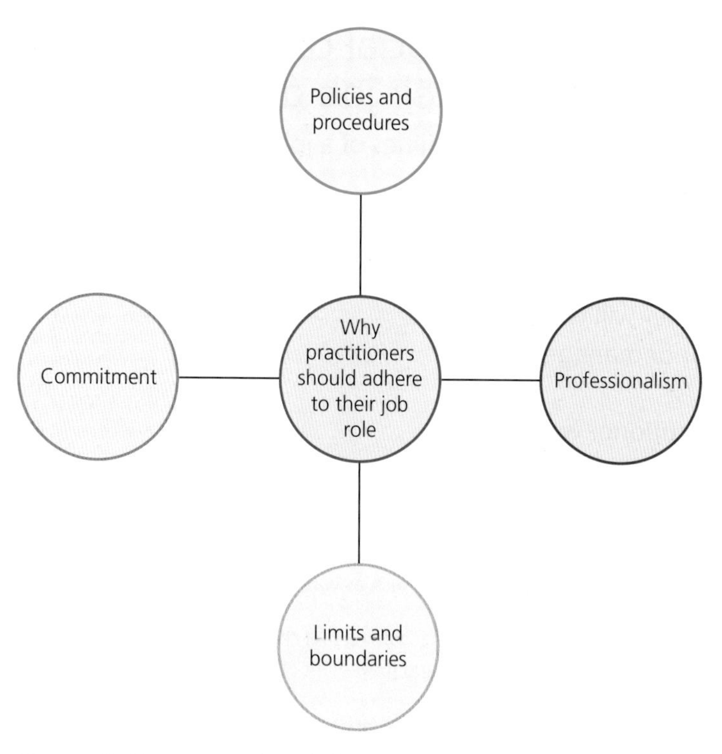

Figure 2.7 Reasons why it is important that practitioners adhere to their job role

Policies and procedures

Following policies and procedures is a requirement of the role of a health and social care practitioner. Most policies and procedures are in place to protect service providers and service users from harm and to protect their rights. Some examples of policies and procedures are those relating to:

- **confidentiality**
- disposal of hazardous waste
- equal opportunities
- **manual handling**
- reporting of accidents
- risk assessments
- **safeguarding**
- storage and dispensing of medicines.

Jargon buster

Confidentiality – limits access or places restrictions on sharing certain types of sensitive information, such medical records, so that it is kept private and available only to those who need to be aware of it.

Manual handling – using the correct procedures when physically moving any load by lifting, putting down, pushing or pulling; for example, transferring a client from a chair into bed.

Safeguarding – actions taken to protect individuals by facilitating a safe and healthy environment.

Policies also ensure that care settings and organisations are complying with the requirements of legislation and it is a legal requirement that care practitioners follow their organisation's policies and procedures. (For more about legislation, see pages 68–78.) By following the setting's policies and procedures, care practitioners can be certain they are delivering safe and appropriate care of the best possible standard for individuals.

Staff who do not follow policies and procedures may place individuals at risk. Failure to follow regulations and procedures could, for example, result in an accident where a client is injured or is given incorrect medication. In serious cases such as these, an individual or the care setting can be taken to court and fined. An individual may be dismissed from their job and the care setting could be closed down.

Professionalism

Professionalism refers to carrying out a job role in a skilful and knowledgeable way and behaving in way that is appropriate and acceptable for the job role. Team work contributes to professional practice.

Practitioners are expected to carry out their tasks to a high standard and professional conduct is integral to their role at all times.

Limits and boundaries

Boundaries are the limits an individual must work within when carrying out a job role. Professional boundaries set limits for safe, acceptable and effective behaviour by practitioners. The job description indicates the scope and type of work involved and this will be reflected by the qualifications and experience required.

Key aspects of limits and boundaries:

- **Client focus** – practitioners should place the needs of the client at the centre of any decisions that are made about them, their care or their lives; decisions should not be based on the needs of the practitioner, such as lack of time or available staff.
- **Self-disclosure** – the practitioner should not give out information about themselves and their personal life to clients.
- **Working within own competence** – practitioners must understand the limits of their role and of their own personal capabilities and know when to refer an issue to their supervisor or manager.

Health and social care practitioners should only carry out the tasks that are part of their job description. They should not attempt to carry out tasks that they have not been trained for, such as manual handling, as they may be putting themselves and others at risk of harm.

Activity

Good time keeping is an important aspect of professionalism. Write an explanation of why good time keeping is important for health and social care practitioners.

Commitment

A commitment is a promise or agreement to do something. It is the responsibility that care workers and practitioners in health and social care services have for those in their care: to perform the tasks and carry out the responsibilities of their particular job role to the required standard and for the benefit of their service users.

1.3 Why continuing professional development is integral to the role of the health and social care practitioner

Continuing professional development (CPD) refers to ongoing learning and skills development. Ongoing learning is essential, or 'integral', to the role of a health and social care professional throughout their career. It ensures that an individual's practice, skills and knowledge are always up to date and meet the required standards.

Continuing professional development does not just occur by attending courses but also through experience, self-study and sharing best practice.

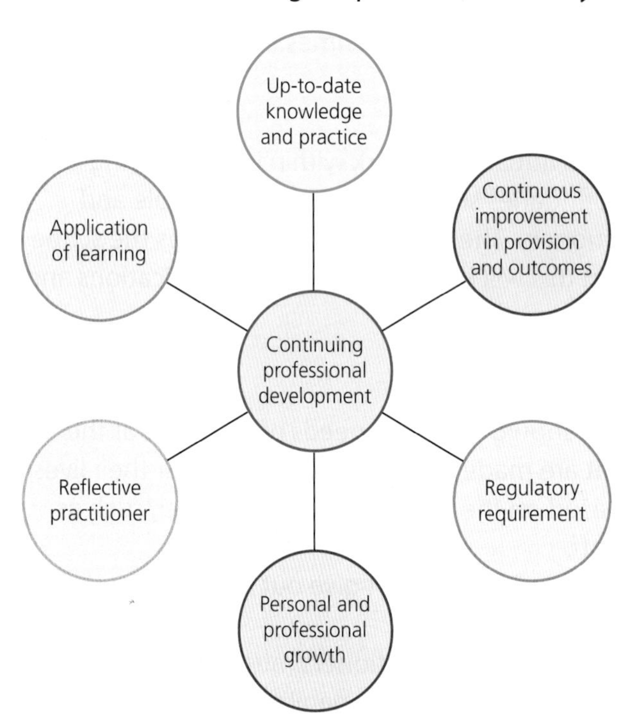

Figure 2.8 Importance of continuing professional development

Up-to-date knowledge and practice

Practitioners need to keep themselves up to date about:

- **best practice**
- lessons learned from poor practice
- legislation and any changes
- new ways of working.

Care organisations have a responsibility to ensure staff have opportunities to receive relevant training for the knowledge and skills required by their job role. Practitioners have a duty to ensure that they attend training and take advantage of opportunities to improve their practice.

Jargon buster

Best practice – procedures or ways of working that are accepted as being the best and most effective methods to use.

Continuous improvement in provision and outcomes

Continuous improvement in provision and outcomes is supported by CPD. Care settings that devote time and resources to provide professional development opportunities for their staff will enable them to become committed, well trained and informed practitioners. This can only benefit those individuals who access the care and support services provided by the staff, resulting in positive outcomes.

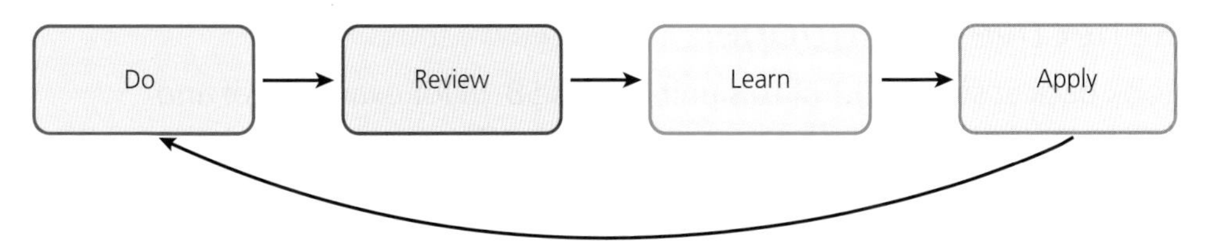

Figure 2.9 A cycle of continuous improvement

The 'Theory in action – Reflective practice and professional development' box on page 67 demonstrates the benefits of CPD for both care practitioners and service users.

Regulatory requirement

It is essential that practitioners and their care settings meet regulatory requirements. As explained in Unit 1 (pages 46–50), inspections are carried out by regulators such as the CQC and Ofsted to monitor whether services are safe, effective and well-managed, and whether they meet the needs of their service users. There can be serious consequences for care settings or practitioners who do not meet the required standards. Having well trained staff who have opportunities for professional development, enabling them to be aware of and able to deliver best practice, is essential to meet the required standards of care.

Personal and professional growth

Personal and professional development results from being able to reflect on your work and care practice in order to assess your own knowledge, skills and practice and be able to identify areas of success and those needing improvement. Willingness and interest in gaining new skills and updating existing skills and knowledge is an important aspect of personal and professional growth.

Ways of ensuring personal and professional growth include:

- accessing additional training available from the care setting
- working closely with a mentor – usually a more experienced colleague who will share their knowledge and skills, give advice, guidance, answer questions and provide feedback on your practice
- observing experienced colleagues or asking them to observe you in order to ask questions and gain feedback
- reflective practice.

All of these methods will help to improve a practitioner's knowledge, skills, competence and care practice.

Reflective practitioner

Look back at section 1.1 of this unit (pages 58–9) for examples of and information about reflective practice and the 'Theory in action' box about reflective practice on page 60.

Application of learning

CPD is not an optional extra; it is essential for practitioners to keep their skills and knowledge updated. If a care practitioner qualifies after three years' training and then continues to work until retirement they will have a career that lasts over 40 years. Learning does not stop when you qualify – it will continue throughout your whole career. There are many frequent changes in health and social care which all practitioners need to keep up to date with. You will need to have a commitment and willingness to apply yourself to continued learning throughout your working life for the benefit of your service users as well as your own job satisfaction.

Theory in action

Reflective practice and professional development

Angela is the Practice Manager at a local GP surgery. Part of her job is to regularly check the patient feedback forms completed by people using the surgery.

Angela finds that recently several older patients have written on their patient feedback forms that they don't always understand the medical terminology used and this makes them feel anxious but they do not like to challlenge it.

To address this problem Angela reflects on her own practice when speaking with patients and discusses the issue with other surgery staff. Angela reaches the conclusion that she, and the other members of staff at the surgery, would benefit from some training in effective communication skills. She thinks that this training will improve everyone's knowledge and understanding about effective communication with patients.

Topics covered by the training Angela organises include:

- active listening
- adapting communication to the needs of the individual
- using straightforward language.

Angela also arranges for a hearing loop to be fitted at the surgery reception desk so that those patients with a hearing impairment do not have to ask for information to be repeated.

Two months later, when checking patient feedback forms again, Angela finds that there are no complaints about communication. Instead, there are some very positive comments from patients about how they have been treated with respect and how useful the hearing loop has been.

Questions

1. Write down these four aspects of reflective practice as headings:
   - Evaluating specific incidents or activities
   - Identifying what might be done better next time
   - Identifying what went well
   - Exploring training and development needs

   Under each heading, list the actions that demonstrate Angela's reflective practice.
2. Explain how this has contributed to Angela's continuing professional development.
3. How has Angela's reflective practice helped to improve provision and outcomes for individuals?

■ Learning outcome 2: Understand health and social care values underpinning practice (P1, P3, P7, M2, D1)

High priority

Make sure you know:

- legislation that impacts on practice in care settings
- regulations that impact on practice in care settings
- the names of health and social care values
- examples of how practitioners apply the care values in their daily work
- a definition of person-centred practice
- the impact of person-centred practice on an individual's health and wellbeing.

2.1 Legislation and standards which underpin practice

All practitioners should be aware of the legislation and standards that govern health and social care provision.

Legislation

Legislation protects all groups of people in society. It provides individuals with rights to which they are entitled through laws passed by parliament. Legislation enables care providers to deliver services in a controlled, structured and safe manner. Legislation is upheld through the courts; it supports an individual's rights and also states their responsibilities to society.

Key factors of legislation in relation to health and social care:

- Imposes responsibilities on service providers to promote equal opportunities and to support individual rights.
- Aims to prevent **direct** and **indirect discrimination** and unfair treatment.
- Provides a framework to maintain and improve quality of practice.
- Provides guidance for those who work in the health and social care sectors.
- Sets out the standard of practice and conduct required by those who work in the health and social care sectors.

Legislation enables individuals to take action against discrimination and poor practice through the courts to obtain **redress**.

Jargon buster

Direct discrimination – intentionally putting someone at a disadvantage or treating them unfairly based on their age, gender or race, for example.

Indirect discrimination – when a policy, practice or a rule applies to everybody but has a detrimental effect on some people. For example, if a job advert stated that male applicants must be clean shaven, this would discriminate against individuals whose religious beliefs require them to have a beard.

Redress – to put something right, for example an individual obtaining justice after receiving inadequate care. Redress may take the form of compensation awarded by the courts or the individual having their rights restored in some way.

General Data Protection Regulation (GDPR)

The General Data Protection Regulation (GDPR) is a set of EU-wide data protection rules that have been brought into UK law as the Data Protection Act 2018 (see Table 2.1). This law applies to the processing of data by care organisations and settings. Processing data is the act of obtaining, recording or using an individual's personal information.

The GDPR sets out seven key principles:

- **Lawfulness, fairness and transparency** – this means that people have a right to know and view any information that is being held about them, to know how their information is being used, to have any errors corrected, and to prevent any data being used for advertising or marketing.
- **Purpose limitation** – information should only be collected for a specific purpose. Organisations such as the NHS and health and social care settings can hold information about staff and clients for a clear purpose and must only use it for that purpose.
- **Data minimisation** – data collection should be limited to that which is necessary and relevant to the purpose. This means that organisations and care settings must not collect unnecessary information that is not relevant.
- **Accuracy** – data found to be inaccurate should be destroyed or corrected. Staff have a responsibility to ensure information they collect and use is correct and up to date.
- **Storage limitation** – this means that information should be kept for no longer than necessary. Data should be deleted or destroyed when it is no longer needed – for example, staff should securely delete or shred sensitive or personal data.

- **Integrity and confidentiality (security)** – information must be held and processed securely, so in care settings access should be restricted. For example, non-authorised staff/people should not be allowed to access the information; it should be kept in secure conditions and stored safely, such as in a locked filing cabinet. Electronic records should be password protected to limit access.
- **Accountability** – care organisations must have appropriate systems and records in place to demonstrate they are complying with the Regulations. They must be able to demonstrate how they gained an individual's consent for processing their information. If there is a serious breach of an individual's data, there is a duty to inform the individual straight away.

Table 2.1 Summary of individual rights provided by GDPR

Individual right	Meaning for individuals
Right to be informed	Must be told data is being collected
Right of access	Must be allowed to see the data held
Right to rectification	Inaccurate information must be corrected
Right to erasure	Can request the deletion of data
Right to restrict processing	Can request data is not used
Right to data portability	Can request their data (usually digital) is transferred between organisations
Right to object	Can stop their data from being used
Rights related to automated decision-making including profiling	There are controls about the automated collection and use of data

Human Rights Act 1998

The Human Rights Act 1998 applies to all public authorities. A public authority is an organisation that has a public function, for example care homes run by local authorities and hospitals. Through a series of Articles, the Act sets out rights to which everyone is entitled. Some of the rights are particularly relevant to health and social care:

- **Right to life** – services such as the NHS provide medication and treatments to preserve life.
- **Right to respect, privacy and family life** – enable individuals to live as independently as they can, providing dignity and respect for individual needs.
- **Right to liberty and security** – an individual cannot be detained or deprived of their freedom unless they have committed a serious crime or have been appropriately assessed with regard to the following legislation:
  - The Mental Health Act
  - The Mental Capacity Act (Deprivation of Liberty).

- **Right to freedom from discrimination** – these rights are further supported by the Equality Act 2010, see below.
- **Right to freedom of expression** – individuals have their own opinions and should have the opportunity to express these. For example, health and social care service users have the right to be consulted and to make choices regarding their care and treatment.
- **Right to freedom of thought, conscience and religion** – an individual has the right to their own faith and beliefs which should be respected.

Equality Act 2010

The Equality Act 2010 simplified previous laws covering discrimination, such as the Sex Discrimination Act, the Race Relations Act and the Disability Discrimination Act. All of these previous laws were brought together in this one new piece of legislation.

Key aspects of the Equality Act:

- Direct and indirect discrimination on the basis of a **protected characteristic** is illegal. The nine protected characteristics are age, disability, gender reassignment, marriage and civil partnership, pregnancy and maternity, race, religion, sex and sexual orientation.
- Discrimination in education, employment, access to goods and services and housing is prohibited.
- Victimisation and **harassment** on the basis of a protected characteristic is prohibited.
- Reasonable adjustments have to be made by employers or providers of goods or services for those with disabilities. For example, installing a ramp to access a building, aids such as computer software to help a person to do their job or providing information in a large format. Hearing loop systems and information provided in Braille are also reasonable adjustments that can enable individuals to access services.
- Women have the right to breastfeed in public places. It is against the law for a woman to receive less favourable treatment because they are breastfeeding when receiving services.
- The Act encourages positive action. One form of positive action is encouraging or training people to apply for jobs or take part in an activity in which people with a protected characteristic, such as disability, are under-represented.
- Discrimination due to association is now an offence. This means that there is now protection from discrimination for carers of an individual who has a protected characteristic.

Jargon buster

Harassment – unwanted behaviour that is intended to intimidate or humiliate someone.

Protected characteristic – refers to nine characteristics of individuals identified by the Equality Act. It is unlawful to discriminate on the basis of a protected characteristic.

Health and Social Care Act 2012

The Health and Social Care Act 2012 is underpinned by two main principles: first, it enables patients to have more control over the care they receive, and second, those responsible for patient care such as the doctors, nurses and others who work in the NHS and social care have the freedom and power to commission care that meets local needs.

Key aspects of the Health and Social Care Act:

- 'No decision about me, without me' is intended to become the guiding principle behind which patients are treated. Patients are able to choose their GP, consultant, treatment and hospital or other local health service. They should be consulted and fully involved in the process of planning their care.
- Clinical commissioning groups are groups of general practices that work together in a local area to commission services to achieve the best possible care for individuals.
- Health and Wellbeing Boards bring together health and social care and are made up of commissioners, councillors and lay (non-medical) representatives to promote joint working and tackle inequalities in people's health and wellbeing.
- An increased focus on public health and prevention. Local councils have taken over responsibility for public health services and population health improvement, for example in relation to obesity, anti-smoking, screening and vaccinations.
- Healthwatch is an independent service created by the Act, which aims to protect the interests of all those who use health and social care services. Healthwatch has a role in communicating the views of patients to commissioning bodies and regulators.

Check what you know

'No decision about me, without me' is a quote from the Health and Social Care Act 2012.

What does this statement mean for individuals and their families who access care services?

Care Act 2014

This Act relates to those being assessed or receiving social care, and those who care for them.

Key aspects of the Care Act 2014:

- There is a duty on local authorities to promote an individual's 'wellbeing'. The wellbeing principles include: personal dignity, protection from abuse and neglect, physical, mental health and emotional wellbeing, social and economic wellbeing, suitability of living accommodation and control by the individual over day-to-day life (including in relation to care and support). This means that whenever a local authority makes a decision about an adult, it must promote that adult's wellbeing.
- Continuity of care must be provided if someone moves from one area to another, so that there is no gap in care or support when an individual moves.
- There is a duty on local authorities to carry out a Child's Needs Assessment (CNA) for young people where there is likely to be a need for care and support after they reach the age of 18.
- An independent advocate is to be available to facilitate the involvement of an adult or carer who is the subject of an assessment, care or support planning or a review.
- Adult safeguarding. This includes responsibility to ensure enquiries are made into cases of abuse and neglect, the establishment of Safeguarding Adults Boards and responsibility to ensure information sharing and inter-professional working.
- Local authorities have to guarantee preventative services which could help reduce or delay the development of care and support needs, including carers' support needs.

Activity

Create a concept map of facts about each of the legislation described above to help you to remember the content of each.

Standards

Standards are rules and regulations that set out expected ways of working, professional conduct and practice, for care services and practitioners. Examples of different types of standards that apply to health and social care are detailed below.

Codes of practice

A code of practice (sometimes called a code of conduct) is a set of rules that outlines the agreed ways of working and approach that care workers should follow in their work. Codes of practice provide a clear set of standards that care practitioners are expected to meet. An example of a code of practice is shown in Figure 2.10.

As a Healthcare Support Worker or Adult Social Care Worker in England you must:

1. Be accountable by making sure you can answer for your actions or omissions.
2. Promote and uphold the privacy, dignity, rights, health and wellbeing of people who use health and care services and their carers at all times.
3. Work in collaboration with your colleagues to ensure the delivery of high quality, safe and compassionate healthcare, care and support.
4. Communicate in an open, and effective way to promote the health, safety and wellbeing of people who use health and care services and their carers.
5. Respect a person's right to confidentiality.
6. Strive to improve the quality of healthcare, care and support through continuing professional development.
7. Uphold and promote equality, diversity and inclusion.

Figure 2.10 Code of Conduct for Healthcare Support Workers and Adult Social Care Workers in England (source: Skills for Care & Skills for Health)

A code of practice helps practitioners to:

- know the standards they are expected to meet
- know whether they are working to the standards or if they need to change the way they are working
- identify areas for continuing professional development
- fulfil the requirements of their role, behave correctly and do the right thing at all times. This is essential to protect people who use health and care services from harm.

A code of practice helps service users to:

- understand what standards they can expect from care workers
- have confidence that they will be treated with dignity, respect and compassion at all times.

A code of practice helps employers to:

- understand what standards they should expect from their staff
- identify care workers who do not meet the standards
- identify support and training needs of their staff.

Find out more

Codes of practice

Carry out some internet research to find examples of different codes of practice – some suggested links are shown below.

Care Quality Commission Code of practice on confidential personal information:

www.cqc.org.uk/get-involved/consultations/code-practice-confidential-personal-information

Health and Care Professions Council – includes codes of practice for 6 health and care professions:

www.hcpc-uk.org/about-us/who-we-regulate/the-professions

Jargon buster

Control measures – actions that can be taken to reduce the risks posed by a hazard or to remove the hazard altogether.

Risk assessment – the process of evaluating the likelihood of a hazard causing harm.

Regulations

Regulations are rules that are set out in law; it is a legal requirement that these must be followed or the care setting will be breaking the law. Regulations have a major influence on the way that care settings provide care. Some examples of regulations that apply to a care setting are described in Table 2.2.

Table 2.2 Regulations that care settings must follow

Regulation	What it means for care settings
Manual Handling Operations Regulations 2002 Lifting Operations and Lifting Equipment Regulations (LOLER) 1998	These Regulations ensure staff are trained in moving and handling activities, including lifting, lowering, pushing, pulling and carrying, so they are carried out safely. This would include using equipment such as hoists or slide boards to assist with transferring individuals in care settings in and out of bed, for example.
Reporting of Injuries, Diseases and Dangerous Occurrences Regulations (RIDDOR) 2013	Lays down rules about the reporting and recording of work-related accidents that cause death or serious injuries, as well as work-related diseases and dangerous occurrences.
Management of Health and Safety at Work Regulations 1999	**Risk assessments** must be carried out and **control measures** put in place. Care settings must appoint a member of staff with responsibility for health, safety and security.
Food Safety (General Food Hygiene) Regulations 1992	Requires care settings to identify food safety hazards and put procedures in place to ensure the safe storage, preparation and serving of food.
Control of Substances Hazardous to Health (COSHH) Regulations 2012	Requires appropriate protective clothing to be provided and worn when handling hazardous substances such as medical waste, cleaning materials and chemicals. Staff must be trained to handle hazardous substances and a COSHH file must be kept which lists all hazardous substances in the workplace.
Health and Social Care Act 2008 (Regulated Activities) Regulations 2014	Includes sets of Regulations that influence care practice and that are monitored by the CQC, such as: • Regulation 9: Person-centred care • Regulation 10: Dignity and respect • Regulation 12: Safe care and treatment • Regulation 14: Meeting nutritional and hydration needs

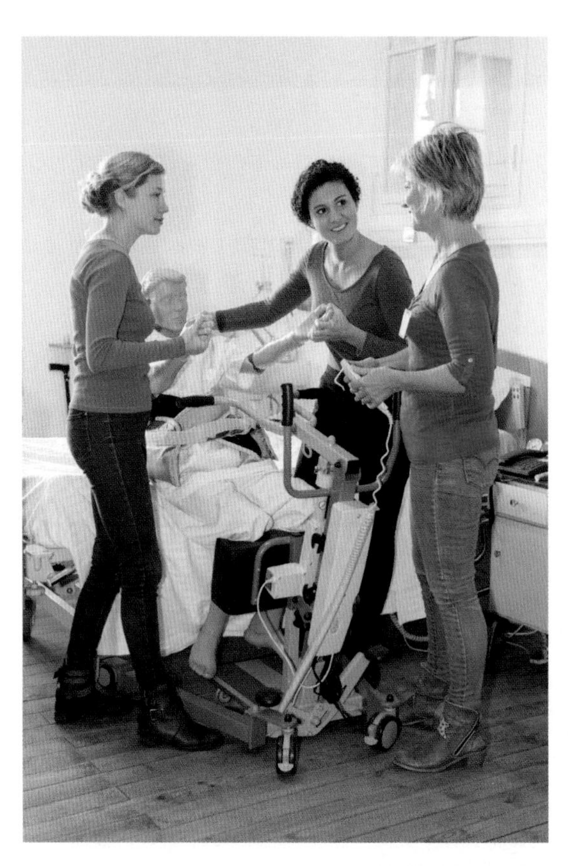

Figure 2.11 Nurses learning to use equipment to lift a patient from a hospital bed

Activity

Make a copy of Table 2.2. Cut up the table so that each Regulation and its corresponding impact on care settings is mixed up. Try to match each Regulation with the correct impact.

Find out more

Regulations

Find out more about the following regulations by using the links below.

CQC Regulations:

www.cqc.org.uk/guidance-providers/regulations-enforcement/regulations-service-providers-managers

Reporting of Injuries, Diseases and Dangerous Occurrences Regulations (RIDDOR):

www.hse.gov.uk/riddor/index.htm

National Occupational Standards (NOS)

National Occupational Standards (NOS) are statements of the standards of performance individuals must achieve and they provide the means for assessing how well an individual can do their job; they describe best practice.

NOS are work-related statements of the ability, knowledge, understanding and experience that an individual should have in order to carry out key tasks competently and effectively.

The NOS for Health and Social Care can be found at: www.ukstandards.org.uk

SCDHSC0214 – Support individuals to eat and drink

Performance criteria: Make preparations to support individuals to eat and drink

You must be able to:

P1 Examine the **care or support plan** to confirm the **individual's** requirements and preferences

P2 Work with the individual, **key people** and **others** to identify the level of support the individual requires and prefers when eating and drinking

P3 Support the individual to **communicate** preferences for food and drink options, taking into account religious, cultural and **dietary requirements** and the individual's plan of care

P4 Acquire any **specialist equipment** and protective coverings that are required to enable the individual to eat and drink

P5 Prepare the environment so that it makes eating and drinking enjoyable and safe

Figure 2.12 National Occupational Standard for preparing to support an individual to eat and drink (source: developed by Skills for Care and Development)

Activity

Think about situations and tasks when manual handling is a necessary part of working in health and social care services. Create one list of situations and tasks for a nurse working on a hospital ward and another for a care assistant providing personal care in someone's home.

Check what you know

Write four facts about National Occupational Standards for Health and Social Care.

The 6Cs

The 6Cs are:

- care
- compassion
- competence
- communication
- courage
- commitment.

The 6Cs are key principles which should inform every health and social care worker's practice:

- **Care** – a care worker will do all they can to maintain or improve an individual's health and wellbeing.
- **Compassion** – being able to provide care and support with kindness, consideration, respect and empathy.
- **Competence** – refers to the ability of a care worker to provide high quality, effective care by applying their knowledge, skills, understanding and expertise to meet an individual's care needs.

- **Communication** – essential to developing good relationships with service users, their families and also with colleagues. Being able to listen carefully and speak in a way that individuals receiving care and support can understand.
- **Courage** – being brave and able to speak up about concerns; doing the right thing and also having the courage to try something new, such as new ways of working.
- **Commitment** – a care worker is dedicated to providing care and support to meet the individual's needs.

The Care Certificate sets out the standards that should be covered by induction training before members of the health care and social care support workforce are allowed to work without direct supervision. The 6Cs form part of all the Care Certificate standards.

Extend

Find out more about the Care Certificate and see how the 6Cs are a part of each of the 15 Care Certificate standards.

www.skillsforcare.org.uk/Learning-development/inducting-staff/care-certificate/Care-Certificate.aspx

Check what you know

1. Name the 6Cs.
2. Give an example of how a care worker could demonstrate each of the 6Cs.

2.2 Health and social care values

The values of care are core principles that underpin the work of those providing health and social care services. Applying the values of care ensures that individuals using health and social care environments receive appropriate person-centred care.

Table 2.3 explains some of the health and social care values that are essential for person-centred care.

Table 2.3 Health and social care values

Care value	Explanation
Duty of care	Refers to the legal obligation professionals have to protect individuals who they care and support from danger, harm and abuse.
Safeguarding	Refers to the actions taken by care workers to protect individuals by reducing the risks of danger, harm and abuse.
Person-centred approach	Ensures that an individual is supported to make choices and to be involved and in control of their care. The person is at the centre of their care.
Partnership working	This involves different professionals, services and agencies working together in order to provide the best care for an individual.
Dignity	Care that respects and values the individual's rights and needs.
Respect	Having regard for the feelings, opinions, wishes and rights of others; taking into account an individual's differences and treating them accordingly.
Rights of individuals	Everyone has rights. Rights are set out by legislation such as the Equality Act and the Human Rights Act. Practitioners who support an individual's rights will be working within the law and providing a high standard of personalised care.
Confidentiality	Privacy of information limits access or places restrictions on sharing certain types of sensitive information such as a patient's health records, so that it is kept private and available only to those who need to be aware of it to provide appropriate care and support. This is known as sharing information on a 'need to know' basis.
Independence	Not relying on others. An individual having the freedom to make their own decisions. A care worker supports individuals to have as much control over their lives as possible.

Activity

1 On a large piece of plain paper, make a spider diagram of the care values.
2 Extend each of the values by writing examples of how the value would be applied by a practitioner in a care setting.

2.3 How individuals accessing health and social care services are valued

The care values can be applied by care workers in a range of everyday situations and during daily routines. The examples below show how care values are applied during mealtimes, while providing personal care, during activities and with decision-making. They demonstrate how individuals are valued and enabled to be as independent as possible through **person-centred care** on a daily basis.

Jargon buster

Person-centred care – focusing care on the needs of the individual. Ensuring that people's needs are met and they can make informed decisions about their care.

Mealtimes

Having dietary and cultural food needs met and being able to have a drink and feed themselves as independently as possible is important for an individual's health and recovery. It also plays a huge role in a service user's feelings of wellbeing and dignity.

Examples of how a care service can demonstrate care values at mealtimes:

- Care services ensure a range of food is available to meet dietary and cultural needs, including for example Halal, Kosher, vegetarian, gluten-free.
- Care home staff offer privacy for those having difficulties eating, for example individuals can eat in their room if they prefer, or with assistance, if required.
- A choice of meal times is offered.
- Food available and accessible between mealtimes.
- Easy grip knives and forks provided for service users with conditions such as arthritis, fractured wrist, hand tremors, weak grip and loss of strength.
- Enlarged print menus, menu in different languages, or staff reading the menu out, as required by service users.
- Avoid making assumptions about an individual's preferences on the basis of their cultural background – they should be asked what their preferences are.

Theory in action

Providing care that values individuals

Beth is in hospital. The health care assistant has checked Beth's records and knows that she has difficulty swallowing and has a visual impairment so her eyesight is not too good.

Read the conversation below between the health care assistant and Beth and then answer the questions that follow.

Health care assistant: I've got the menu, Beth. I'm hungry, are you?

Beth: Yes I am. Is the food nice here?

Health care assistant: It's not too bad, the fish and chips are really good.

Beth: I used to like fish and chips but I keep getting bones stuck in my throat!

Health care assistant: Well, we've got carrot and tomato soup or pate for starters. I think I will be having the soup, what about you?

Beth: I think I will have the soup – it will go down easily.

Health care assistant: Good choice. Let's see what's on for mains. I'm in luck – the fish and chips are on. Now what have they got that you would like Beth? There's sausage and mash, steak and kidney pie or macaroni cheese.

→

Beth: I haven't had macaroni cheese for ages, I'll have that.

Health care assistant: Great, I'll get those ordered for you.

Questions

1 Revisit Figure 2.12 which shows the National Occupational Standard for supporting individuals to eat and drink. Has the care provided by the health care assistant met the standard? Give reasons for your answer.

2 Explain how the care worker has provided care that values Beth and meets her needs at mealtimes. Consider the following in your answer: dignity, respect, rights, independence, effective communication, person-centred approach to care.

Personal care

Personal care involves tasks that are non-medical. This includes bathing or showering, dressing and going to the toilet. Personal care is an important part of daily living and it is important that practitioners consider the needs, preferences and feelings of those receiving this type of care. Applying values of care such as respect and dignity are essential.

Examples of how a care service can demonstrate care values during personal care:

- Always ask if it is okay before working with an individual.
- Explain what needs to be done before doing it, how it will be done and why.
- Talk with the client to reassure and help them feel at ease.
- Show respect by asking their permission before entering their personal space.
- Provide practical help and assistance only where needed, in order to encourage independence.
- Provide privacy, for instance by drawing curtains, using a screen and closing the bathroom door as this shows respect.
- Clothing or hospital gowns should always be arranged in a dignified way.
- Use aids when assisting with dressing, explaining/demonstrating how to use them, for example leg lifters, zip pullers, sock helpers or button loops; this helps to promote independence.
- Take the individual's lifestyle choices into consideration. Respect their choice of dress or hairstyle, for example.

Extend

Read the conversation below between Joanna (a care assistant) and Mrs Clark (a 75-year-old woman living in a residential care home).

Joanna: Now come on, Mrs C. You know you like to get up early for breakfast and have a nice cup of tea at 7 o'clock, so you need to get dressed now.

Mrs Clark: I do wish you would call me Rita.

Joanna: Now don't be silly, you know I always call you Mrs C.

Mrs Clark: Do you think I could wear that green dress I like, the one with the flower pattern?

Joanna: [sighs] I can't see it. Here – have this blue dress instead. It's nice.

Mrs Clark: [frowning] Oh okay then. But it's not as comfortable.

Joanna: Then when you've finished putting that on, we'll get you into the dining room in time for a nice cup of tea before breakfast.

Mrs Clark: But it's only 7 a.m.! I wanted to pop next door to see how Jenny's feeling today. She wasn't feeling too good yesterday.

Joanna: Look, I haven't got time you know. I'm only here until 7.30, so we've got to get you ready for breakfast before I go. And I thought it would be nice for you to sit down in the dining room together with the others for half an hour. You can have a chat.

Mrs Clark: Oh well, if you say so.

1 Write an explanation of the ways in which Joanna has *not* provided care that values Mrs Clark as an individual.
2 Write an alternative script for the same conversation between Joanna and Mrs Clark. Your script should demonstrate ways that Joanna could value Mrs Clark with a person-centred approach when providing care.

Activities

Activities in health and social care settings support an individual's physical and mental health. They provide opportunities to interact and communicate with others and to develop new skills and friendships. Activities can support recovery from an injury or illness as well as providing stimulation and enjoyment for older adults who have moved into residential care, for example.

Examples of how a care service can demonstrate care values during activities:

- Provide activities to meet the different needs of service users, for example **reminiscence therapy**, life story books, yoga, art, reading group, music, cycling, gardening, exercise class, swimming, crossword puzzles, quiz.
- Providing support to ensure everyone can be involved if they want to be, such as someone to assist services users, or physical aids or adaptations such as ramps.
- All activities must be risk assessed to ensure safety of the participants.
- Supervision of activities to ensure safety requirements are being met, to check if participants are enjoying the activity and not becoming distressed or overwhelmed, and to see if any extra support is needed.

Jargon buster

Reminiscence therapy – this involves the use of photographs, music and familiar objects to enable an individual to talk about and share their past life experiences. It is often used with individuals who have dementia, supporting them to interact with others.

Decision-making

To promote the dignity of all individuals they should be fully involved in any decision that affects their care, including personal decisions (such as what to eat, what to wear and what time to go to bed) and wider decisions about their care or support.

Individuals should be supported to make decisions about the services and type of care they want. By applying values of care such as safeguarding, partnership working and promoting independence, practitioners can give individuals support to make their own decisions about their care, so that they can live their lives the way they want to.

Examples of how a care service can demonstrate care values during decision-making:

- Discuss options for care or treatments with clients.
- Provide the necessary information so that individuals can make informed decisions.
- Provide a choice of GP or choice of where to receive treatment or care.
- Ask a client what clothes they would like to wear today.
- Provide a choice of food to meet the client's individual preferences and needs.

Extend

Ben's day

Ben lives in a small residential home with five other people. Ben has physical and learning disabilities. He requires full support for his physical, social and emotional wellbeing. This is his description of a typical day in his life.

> *I spend the morning sitting in the lounge watching TV. The news is on – it must be my favourite programme because I watch it every day.*
>
> *At lunchtime I am taken to sit in the same seat every day, next to the same people, so they must be my friends. I have the same type of meal everyday – something soft and easy to swallow, not sure what it is. I spend most days like this. It would be nice to go out for the day and meet some new people, but the staff really are very busy and so it would be difficult for them to take me out.*
>
> *At teatime I am given some soup and a cup of tea. They are both lukewarm because I am told that I can't have hot liquids because of something called a risk assessment. I don't know what that means exactly. Some of the others have biscuits with their tea. They look nice. I wonder what they taste like?*
>
> *At bedtime two carers help me into the shower and it is interesting to hear about their night out at the pub. I can't remember when I last went out to a pub, so it was really nice to hear all about it.*

Use examples from Ben's description of his day to explain ways that the care workers could provide care that values Ben and meets his individual needs.

Aspects to consider

The above examples of daily tasks carried out by care workers incorporate the features shown in Figure 2.13 of providing care that values individuals.

These aspects should always be considered when planning and carrying out any type of care for an individual. This will ensure that the care provided will have the individual's best interests at heart.

By following the principles of the care values practitioners in health and social care services will be able to provide high quality, personalised, safe and compassionate care that promotes the rights and meets the needs of service users.

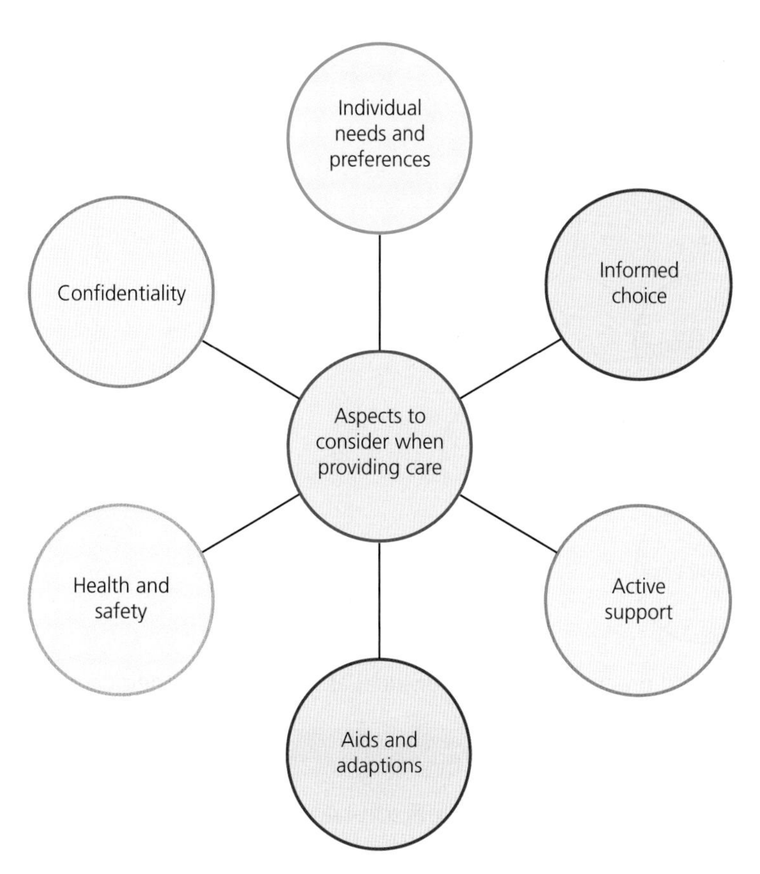

Figure 2.13 Features of care that value individuals

Check what you know

Give five examples of ways practitioners can apply care values during daily practice. They can be related to:

- mealtimes
- personal care
- activities
- decision-making.

2.4 Define person-centred practice

Person-centred practice is about focusing care on the needs of individuals. This means ensuring that an individual's preferences, needs and values guide health and social care decisions, and care is provided that is respectful and responsive to them.

Individuals are put at the centre of the process of identifying their needs and should be involved in all aspects of decision-making (see Figure 2.14).

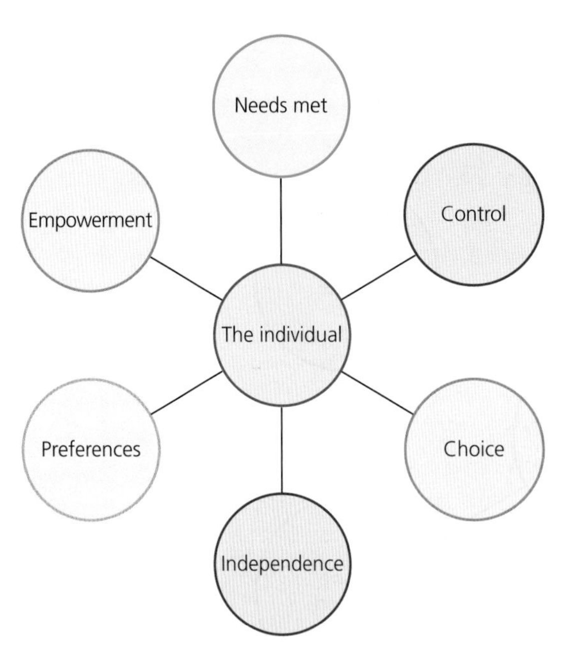

Figure 2.14 Person-centred practice puts the individual at the centre of their care

Check what you know

In your own words, write a definition of 'person-centred practice'.

2.5 Impact for individuals of person-centred practice

Person-centred practice empowers individuals by allowing and encouraging them to have as much control over their care and their lives as possible. If an individual is empowered they will feel more confident and will be able to take more control of their life.

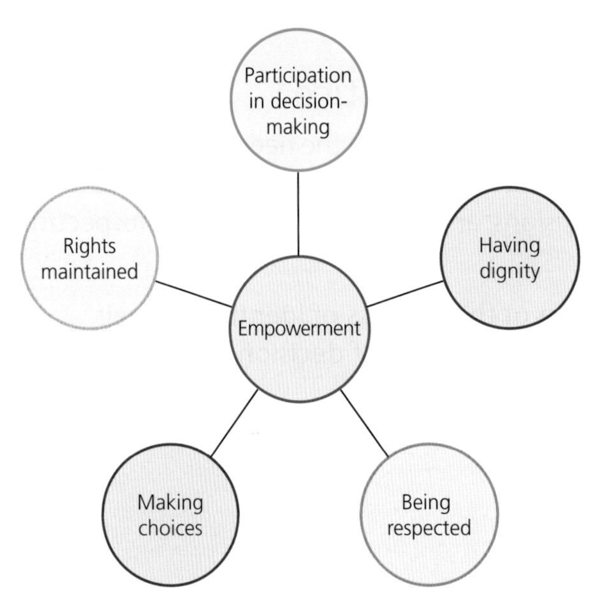

Figure 2.15 Individuals are empowered by person-centred practice

Holistic needs

It is important that practitioners care for the whole person. An illness or physical disability does not just affect the individual physically: it will affect them mentally (or cognitively), emotionally and socially as well as having physical impacts. Think of a time when you have been ill. How did you feel? Did you want to go out and socialise or just stay in and rest in bed? What treatment did you receive? How did it affect you mentally as well as physically?

Holistic means to consider all aspects of something. This means care provided by health and social care practitioners should take into account the whole person, not just their physical symptoms. It is important to care for the whole person and to see them as a person, not just a patient or as a diagnosis of dementia, for example. This leads to a broader idea of care, where the mind, emotions and the body are viewed as an integrated whole – they are all inter-related. This type of care, demonstrated by the person-centred approach, meets the holistic needs of an individual and so will maximise the impact on their health and wellbeing generally, rather than just treating the physical symptoms of their illness.

Meeting individual needs

Meeting an individual's needs will have social, emotional, cognitive and physical impacts for them.

Social impacts

Social impacts relate to an individual's relationships with others. Individuals should be given opportunity for sustained and meaningful interaction that is appropriate to their needs. A person-centred approach will help individuals to gain confidence and make it more likely that she will enjoy the company of others, join in activities and develop friendships with other residents.

Emotional impacts

Emotional impacts relate to an individual's feelings. If hospital patients are not consulted regarding their care, or if staff are too busy to answer questions or explain treatments and medication, then over time the emotional impacts can be significant. This is why person-centred care is so important to ensure the wellbeing of individuals is a priority at all times.

Cognitive impacts

These relate to an individual's mind and their thought processes such as thinking skills, understanding, learning, reasoning and knowledge. A care home resident left in front of the TV every day may lack mental stimulation, lose focus and lack interest in life. They may be having their physical needs met, but not the needs of their mind. Person-centred care will provide a stimulus for the individual to become engaged in activities, keep them interested and involved with life and so avoiding social isolation which can lead to a negative effect on an individual's cognitive wellbeing.

Physical impacts

These relate to an individual's body. Not receiving person-centred care may lead to poor physical health and wellbeing.

Table 2.4 Examples of person-centred practice and its positive impacts

Person-centred practice	Positive impacts of person-centred practice
Asking what the individual would like to drink	This provides the individual with the power to make a decision and gives them a choice, meaning they can choose a drink they will actually drink. It also ensures the individual will take in enough fluids, creating a positive impact on their health. This promotes wellbeing as the individual will feel valued and cared for.
Providing a range of meal choices, including vegetarian, vegan, gluten-free, Kosher and Halal	This ensures everyone in a care setting has adequate nutrition. It also encourages a sense of acceptance and belonging.
Providing opportunities for exercise activities that are appropriate for each individual, along with support to get involved	
Staff should be trained in safeguarding, manual handling and first aid	

Activity

Complete Table 2.4 by adding in the positive impacts for the last two examples of person-centred practice.

Read and write

1. Reread the information in section 2.5 Impact for individuals of person-centred practice, up to and including Table 2.4.
2. Write a short case study of an individual who has care or support needs, for example an individual with hearing or sight loss, dementia or mobility difficulties.
3. List the individual's needs and give examples of person-centred practice that would help to meet these needs.

Extend

Explain how practitioners who provide person-centred care meet the holistic needs of individuals.

1. Revisit the case study you wrote for the 'Read and write' activity above.
2. Write an explanation of how person-centred practice would meet that individual's holistic needs.

Check what you know

For each aspect of empowerment shown in Figure 2.15, give an example of its impact on the health and wellbeing of an individual.

Learning outcome 3: Understand partnership working in health and social care (P8, M3, D2)

High priority

Make sure you know:

- the difference between a working and a personal relationship
- how health and social care practitioners work in partnership
- how partnership working meets individuals' needs
- barriers to partnership working
- how to overcome barriers to partnership working.

3.1 Distinguish between a working relationship and a personal relationship

Health and social care professionals work as part of a team and this often involves working with many different agencies and individuals in order to achieve the best outcome for those receiving care and support. Understanding the differences between working relationships and personal relationships is essential in health and social care.

Table 2.5 Differences between working and personal relationships

Working relationships	Personal relationships
• Working relationships are those between professionals such as a GP, social worker, pharmacist, nurse, CQC inspectors and clients/service users and their family and friends. • A working relationship also exists between members of staff.	• Personal relationships exist between friends, acquaintances, neighbours, partners, family members and relations.
• Working relationships are planned and occur as part of the job role: working with others in order to provide care for individuals.	• Personal relationships develop naturally, for example those with family members. • Friendships gradually develop with people whom you choose to be your friends.
• Clear boundaries are in place and guidelines will be provided such as codes of conduct and a job description. (See also Unit 2, Learning outcome 1, section 1.2, page 61.) • Procedures will be in place that outline agreed ways of working, for example for safeguarding, duty of care and appearance. • There will be policies relating to health and safety, bullying and equal opportunities.	• Personal relationships are not guided by official rules, regulations or policies.
• Confidentiality is very important. • There will be restrictions on sharing certain types of sensitive information, such as a patient's health records, so that it is kept private and available only to those who need to be aware of it in order to provide appropriate care and support. This is known as sharing information on a 'need to know' basis.	• Personal information is shared between family members and friends: this is one of the ways close bonds are developed. ➜

Working relationships	Personal relationships
• Working relationships are underpinned and guided by health and social care values. (See also Learning outcome 2, section 2.2, page 79.)	• While friends and family members generally do respect and value each other and there are expectations that they will support each other, meeting these expectations is voluntary and not a requirement of law.
• Uniform or dress codes may have to be followed. • Attendance and punctuality at work will be monitored.	• No uniform is required by family and friends.

Check what you know

1 List four features of working relationships.
2 List four features of personal relationships.

3.2 How health and social care practitioners work in partnership

Multi-agency

Agencies are organisations, such as the police, local authorities, health trusts charities, schools and colleges and community groups, who work together to provide care and support in order to meet an individual's needs.

Theory in action

Janet's story

Janet is four months pregnant. She is attending the antenatal clinic for the first time, after being persuaded to go by her friend, Steph, who is worried about her as she is not eating a healthy diet and appears quite tired and withdrawn.

Questions

1 Which agencies would work together to support Janet?
2 Which practitioners would be involved in supporting Janet?
3 Explain the different types of support Janet would receive from each agency.
4 How would the support meet Janet's individual needs?

Multi-disciplinary

This refers to a group of health and social care practitioners, each with different roles and responsibilities, working together to meet an individual's needs. They are from different 'disciplines'; this means they have different specialist skills and expertise. For example, the team looking after a pregnant woman, depending on her needs, could include a GP, practice nurse, midwife, hospital nurses, obstetrician, health visitor and possibly a social worker and drugs or alcohol support worker. The 'Theory in action' box on 'Team Around the Child' on page 93 demonstrates how a multi-disciplinary team can work together on a specific individual's case.

National and local approaches to safeguarding

Safeguarding refers to actions taken to protect people's health, wellbeing and rights that enable them to be protected from harm, abuse and neglect.

Nationally there are laws in place to protect children and adults. The Children Act (2004) aims to protect children at risk of harm through the use of care orders or emergency protection orders. The Act makes it the duty of practitioners who work with children to follow safeguarding procedures. The Care Act (2014) (see page 73 for further details) covers the safeguarding of adults.

The CQC is a national organisation that works to protect adults using health and social care services. The CQC reports about safeguarding in its inspection reports and awards services an overall rating based on their findings of whether the care setting is considered to be safe. Action can be taken against settings that do not meet the required safeguarding standards. (See Unit 1, Learning outcome 6, page 46 for more information about the actions that can be taken by the CQC.) An extract from the *Statement on CQC's roles and responsibilities for safeguarding children and adults* is shown below.

> The legal framework to protect children is contained in *Working together to safeguard children* (2015). For adults, the Care Act 2014 gave safeguarding adults a legal framework for the first time. However, the overarching objective for both is to enable children and adults to live a life free from abuse or neglect. This cannot be achieved by any single agency. Every organisation and person who comes into contact with a child or adult has a responsibility and a role to play to help keep children and adults safe.
>
> Source: Statement on CQC's roles and responsibilities for safeguarding children and adults, Care Quality Commission, February 2018

Find out more

To find out more about the CQC and safeguarding, use the link below.
www.cqc.org.uk/sites/default/files/20150710_CQC_New_Safeguarding_Statement.pdf

Safeguarding boards

Local safeguarding boards for adults and for children have a legal duty to lead and co-ordinate safeguarding in the local area. They are multi-agency bodies that are set up in every local authority. Safeguarding boards develop local safeguarding policies and procedures for dealing with safeguarding and ensure effective working with partners to help and protect adults and children who are in need of care and support. This includes responsibility to ensure information sharing and multi-agency working.

Local authorities also have a duty to conduct serious case reviews for children and safeguarding adults reviews where death or serious injuries have occurred.

Safeguarding adults boards focus on the prevention of abuse and neglect, and include:

- the safety of people who use services in local health settings, including mental health
- the safety of adults with care and support needs living in social housing
- effective interventions with adults who self-neglect
- the quality of local care and support services
- the effectiveness of prisons in safeguarding offenders
- adult safeguarding and domestic abuse.

Safeguarding children boards focus on:

- protecting children from abuse and maltreatment
- preventing harm to children's health or development
- ensuring children grow up with the provision of safe and effective care
- taking action to enable all children and young people to have the best outcomes.

Check what you know

1 Explain the difference between multi-agency working and multi-disciplinary working.
2 What is the purpose of local safeguarding boards?

Team Around the Child

Team Around the Child (TAC) refers to the group of practitioners working with a particular child or young person and their family. A TAC plans actions around the child/young person's identified but unmet needs through an agreed written TAC plan. The team works together to plan support to address problems in a holistic way. The TAC process starts at the point where a child/young person has been assessed as needing a multi-agency approach.

Principles underpinning the TAC are:

- the child's needs must come first
- the young person and/or parent should always be present during discussions
- the child's or young person's welfare is everyone's responsibility
- all organisations must work together
- the child's or young person's and/or parent(s)'s views must be considered.

Theory in action

Team Around the Child

Jayden is 11 years old and is having problems settling in at his new secondary school and has been excluded twice.

Jayden and his mum have attended a TAC meeting, where the outcomes below were agreed.

Desired outcomes	
Young person (Jayden): • To join a football team • To see family more often • To feel safe in school and not be bullied	Parent (Cheryl): • Jayden not to be bullied at school • Jayden to stop using drugs • Jayden to be in school and not excluded again
Practitioners' goals: • Jayden to be supported to avoid further exclusions • Jayden's health needs to be addressed • Jayden to receive support regarding his substance use • Parenting support for Cheryl (to be addressed at next meeting)	

An 'agreed actions' plan is produced for Jayden:

Desired outcomes	Action	Who will do this	By when?
To join a football team	Identify a suitable local team and make contact. Arrange introductory visit.	Jo Burns – family support worker	Within 10 days of this meeting
	Arrange charity funding for football boots.	Alex Smith – local charity worker	Within two weeks
For bullying to stop	Jayden allocated a safe space to use if he is feeling threatened (yellow card to show staff).	Mr Gallen (Jayden's class tutor) to identify and inform	This week
	Jayden to report all incidents of bullying on the day it happens.	Jayden	Ongoing
	Peer support mentor to be allocated for Jayden – who this should be to be agreed.	Mr Gallen – to discuss with pastoral care lead in school, Mr McAfee	Start in one week
	Jayden given the option to use the library at lunchtimes.	Mrs Hardy (librarian) to set up	This week

Questions

1. List the organisations, practitioners and individuals that are involved in Jayden's TAC meeting and state their roles.
2. Give two examples of how the practitioners/organisations are working together.
3. How does the 'agreed actions' plan show that Jayden's views have been considered and his needs put first?

Extend

How will the 'agreed actions' plan produced in the 'Theory in action – Team Around the Child' box benefit Jayden?

3.3 How partnership working meets the needs of individuals

Partnership working involves practitioners, organisations and families working together for the benefit of the individual who is in need of care and support. The team will work together in order to provide the types of support required to meet an individual's needs. Key principles of partnership working include openness, trust, shared goals and effective communication. It is important that those involved have mutual respect for each other and value each other's skills and knowledge, focusing on working together in the best interests of the individual receiving care and support.

When partnership working is effective, it leads to positive outcomes for those individuals accessing health and social care services. Figure 2.16 explains how working in partnership helps to meet the needs of individuals.

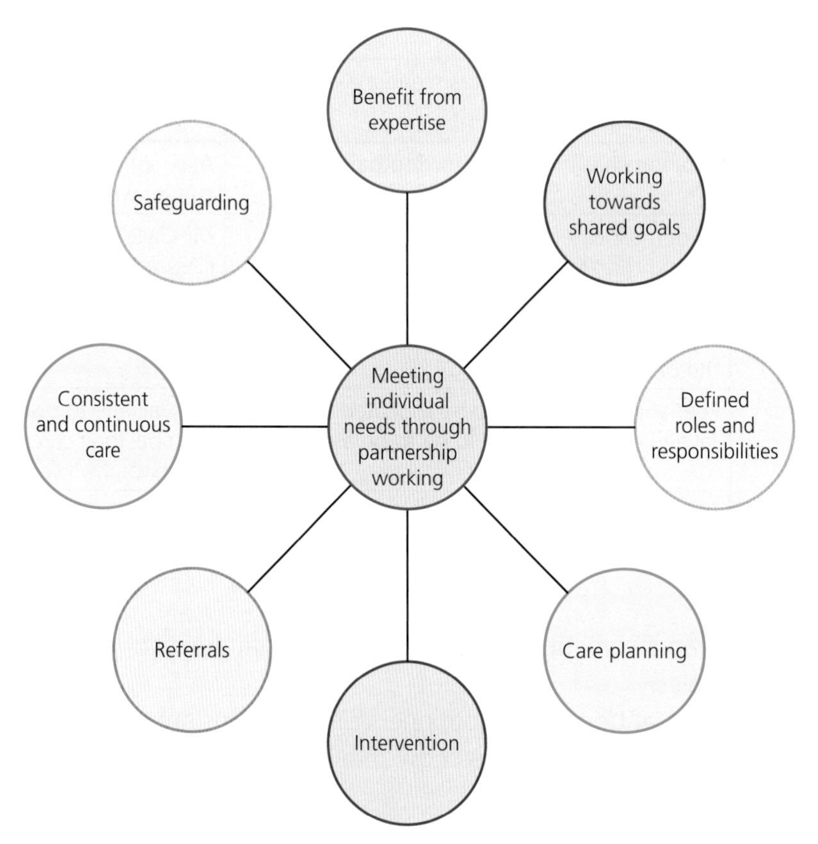

Figure 2.16 How partnership working meets the needs of individuals

3.4 Barriers to partnership working

Barriers to partnership working can lead to unsatisfactory outcomes for both individuals and professionals. Three of the main barriers are described below.

Ineffective communication

Ineffective communication can lead to misunderstandings, frustration or resentment between individuals and professionals. Practitioners may be reluctant to adapt their working practices to meet the particular needs of individuals. Poor communication can also lead to an individual's needs being unmet because everyone assumes someone else is dealing with the situation.

Time management

Time management can be an issue if practitioners do not share information when needed, resulting in delays or preventing care services being provided. It may be difficult for practitioners to attend multi-agency meetings and reviews due to other demands on their time. Timely action in the case of safeguarding situations is essential and lack of action or communication can cost lives.

Resources

A lack of resources can affect the type of care and support that can be provided for individuals. Some specialist care services may only be provided in certain areas. Resources such as money, staff, hospital beds and places in residential care are all in limited supply. An example is an older adult's discharge from hospital being delayed due to a lack of sufficient domiciliary care.

Extend

Look back at the 'agreed actions' plan for Jayden in the 'Theory in action – Team Around the Child' box on page 93. Give examples of barriers to partnership working and how they could affect the plan working for Jayden.

3.5 Strategies to overcome barriers to partnership working

There are a number of strategies that can be used to overcome barriers to partnership working.

- **Effective communication** – you have already looked at the importance of communication – see Unit 1, Learning outcome 3, section 3.3 (pages 28–32) and Unit 2, Learning outcome 1, section 1.1 (pages 55–6).

- **Co-operation** – this is the action or process of a group or team of individuals working together to achieve the same goals.
- **Collaboration** – this means professionals working together; it is a way of pooling expertise, knowledge and experience in order to resolve problems or produce a care plan, for example. This prevents duplication of tasks, which may happen if two practitioners are working in isolation doing the same thing, which is unnecessary and a waste of time and resources.
- **Understand viewpoints** – it is important to understand that practitioners from different agencies will have different perspectives or viewpoints about situations. Each person will look a situation from their own area of expertise, which may be different to that of another type of practitioner. All viewpoints have value and should be listened to and considered in order to reach the best solution for the issue being discussed.
- **Problem solving** – this is where care workers look at a range of solutions to a problem situation and are able to choose the best way to approach the issue in a logical and reasoned manner.
- **Resolution** – this is the process of resolving an issue, conflict or difference of opinion. It usually involves an open discussion, where individuals feel able to express their concerns or feelings, before a solution is reached.

Figure 2.17 Health and social care staff collaborating at a case meeting

Check what you know

1 Give three examples of barriers to partnership working.
2 Suggest a strategy for overcoming each of the barriers you have listed.

Learning outcome 4: Understand different career pathways in the health and social care sector (P5, P6)

High priority

Make sure you know:

- examples of opportunities for career development
- sources of careers information
- different types of qualifications and training available
- the stages involved in creating a personal development plan.

4.1 Opportunities for career development

In this section you will look at the various opportunities that exist for careers in health and social care, and ways that you can explore potential opportunities for career development.

Volunteering

Doing voluntary work is an excellent way of gaining knowledge and experience of an area of health or social care you are interested in. Figure 1.1 in Unit 1 (page 5) shows a range of voluntary organisations relating to health and social care. Doing voluntary work is a good introduction to an area of work that you might be interested in. Gaining experience of working in the care sector can help you to decide whether it is what you want to do in the future. Experience and skills gained will be valued by potential employers when applying for apprenticeships and jobs, and for courses or training in the future.

Education

Most roles will require a minimum of GCSE Maths and English at grade 4 or higher. Many roles in health and social care require some experience, so undertaking voluntary work can be very useful. Depending on the seniority and responsibilities of the role, different qualifications are required. To train as a midwife, for example, you will need to complete a university degree course, entrance to which may require at least five GCSEs at grades 9–4 or A to C (including English and a science subject) and usually three A Levels (Biology may be required by some universities). Individual universities will have their own entry requirements.

Employment

Whether it is a Saturday job, part- or full-time, employment is an opportunity to gain experience and skills in the real world of work. You can learn from more experienced colleagues as well as through any training provided. Many skills are transferable, such as communication skills and team-working skills;

these will be useful whatever future job role you do. Many employers offer on-the-job training which can help to develop your career prospects as your experience and skills increase.

Coaches and mentors are experienced staff that provide one-to-one support and feedback in the workplace and they can advise you on best practice as well as providing training for specific tasks.

Progression

Progression pathway means the route from one course or job role to another. As you gain qualifications, training and experience, you will be able to work your way up to more responsible and more senior job roles. Some people complete qualifications in their own time in order to improve their chances of promotion, both within and outside of the organisation.

Many job roles will require specific degree-level qualifications, for example social work, physiotherapy, nursing and medicine. These require three or more years of study at university. Other routes to professional practice include an apprenticeship.

If a job advertisement states certain skills or qualifications are 'essential' then there is no point applying if you do not have those skills or qualifications, because 'essential' means absolutely necessary. 'Desirable', however, means ideally you would have these skills or qualifications but you will still be considered if you have not. Many employers request that you should be willing to work towards a particular qualification if you are successful in your application for a job.

Five things to know

Opportunities for career development

Make sure you know:

1. why volunteering helps career development
2. the difference between 'essential' and 'desirable' skills or qualifications
3. the benefits of work experience or employment
4. the benefits of working with a mentor
5. that there are many progression routes to achieve the same career goal.

4.2 Sources of information in relation to career development

There are a number of sources of information that can help you in your career development.

Organisations and services

The NHS and social care services provide extensive information about career development opportunities on their websites. Most professional roles within these services have their own websites with careers advice and guidance, for example social work, physiotherapy, nursing and midwifery. Skills for Health (www.skillsforhealth.org.uk) and Skills for Care (www.skillsforcare.org.uk) have comprehensive information on their websites about careers in health and social care.

Schools and colleges have careers libraries and open days or evenings when staff, and sometimes employers, are available to provide advice and information about qualifications and career routes.

Careers advisers

Careers staff in schools and colleges or at a local careers office provide advice. They are professional advisers who are specially trained and can help you to assess your strengths, weaknesses and skills. They can also:

- carry out mock interviews
- provide information about training schemes
- give information about further and higher education courses
- provide information about local employers and job vacancies.

Internet

There are many job sites, employment agencies and recruitment companies on the internet. These can provide information about gaining job skills as well as job vacancies in the local area. Some have advice and information about interviews and general advice on applying for a job.

The NHS and social care services have websites full of detailed information about all the roles available in these sectors.

Many professions such as medicine and nursing have their own websites, which provide careers advice:

- British Medical Association: www.bma.org.uk/advice
- Royal College of Nursing: www.rcn.org.uk
- Royal College of Occupational Therapists: www.rcot.co.uk

Find out more

Careers in health and social care

Use the links below to find out more about health and social care services.

Health care services:

www.healthcareers.nhs.uk/explore-roles

www.jobs.nhs.uk

Social care services:

www.healthcareers.nhs.uk/working-health/working-social-care%20

www.skillsforcare.org.uk/Careers-in-care/job-roles/Job-roles-in-social-care.aspx

Media

Many organisations now use social media to provide information about careers and job vacancies, alongside traditional job adverts in local and national newspapers. The NHS also uses television advertising to highlight staff shortage areas to encourage applications.

Work experience/placement

Provides an opportunity to experience a workplace. Work experience enables you to see what a job entails and whether it is something you would be interested in doing as a career.

4.3 Qualifications and training opportunities in relation to career development

To pursue your chosen career in health and social care, you need to know what qualifications and training you will require. There are a number of ways that you can access qualifications and training, as described below.

Further education

Further education colleges (or FE colleges as they are known) offer a range of qualifications and training such as:

- A Levels
- apprenticeships
- traineeships
- vocational qualifications
- entry-level training and functional skills.

Higher education

Universities and other higher education colleges offer degree courses as well as post-graduate courses, such as a Master's degree.

Apprenticeships

An apprenticeship provides training 'on the job'. An apprenticeship is a good way to gain experience and is an excellent introduction to working in many areas of health and social care. Apprenticeships are available for a very wide range of job roles, from administration, human resources (HR) and accounts to clinical support workers, podiatrists, operating department practitioners and ambulance care assistants.

Apprenticeships range across all levels, including degree level, and many lead to nationally recognised and regulated roles. A midwifery degree-standard apprenticeship is now available. This offers an alternative route to a full-time university course, although you will still need to be able to study at degree standard.

Find out more

Apprenticeships

Use the link below to find out about apprenticeships in health and social care.

www.healthcareers.nhs.uk/career-planning/study-and-training/Apprenticeships-traineeships-and-cadet-schemes

My life as a healthcare support worker

Alex is doing a healthcare support worker apprenticeship. He would like to be a physiotherapist and sees the apprenticeship as a good step on the way to achieve his ambition.

It appealed to me because I didn't have any qualifications and you don't need any for an apprenticeship at this level. I help look after the patients, starting with making sure they're set up and ready for breakfast. I help them eat breakfast if they need help and help them get washed.

I look after patients' general needs throughout the day, helping them move around and regularly turning the patients at risk of developing pressure sores. I carry out clinical observations, too, like taking patients' temperature and blood pressure and carrying out blood sugar checks before mealtimes for patients who are diabetic.

An important part of every day is keeping records of everything I've done for an individual. I was given training about safe practice and my manager made sure I didn't move any patients on my own at first. Now if patients ask for help moving around, I try and encourage them to be independent and to do it themselves first.

The best bit of the job is getting to know the patients on the ward. Depending on the ward, you look after quite a few elderly patients who often have a lot of stories to tell. I know I make a difference just by listening and getting to know them.

Alex's apprenticeship qualification will help him get a physiotherapy assistant job and put him on the path of what he wants to do.

Qualifications and training required for specific roles

Professional job roles require study such as diplomas. Different courses require different qualifications and grades, so it is important to check what is required for a course you are interested in.

The Care Certificate 2014 sets out the minimum standards that should be covered in induction training for members of the health care support and social care workforce before they are allowed to work without direct supervision.

The Care Certificate is for 'unregulated' job roles, rather than professions such as social work or nursing. It is required for roles such as health care assistants, occupational therapy and physiotherapy assistants and social care assistants in residential, domiciliary and day care settings.

The aim of the Care Certificate is for all care workers to have the same skills and knowledge to provide safe and high-quality care and support. The skills are detailed in 15 standards and care workers are assessed against these.

Skills for Health and Skills for Care have comprehensive information on their websites about careers in health and social care and the qualifications required for specific job roles.

Additional information about qualifications and skills for various job roles can be found in Unit 1, Learning outcome 2, section 2.1 (pages 11–22).

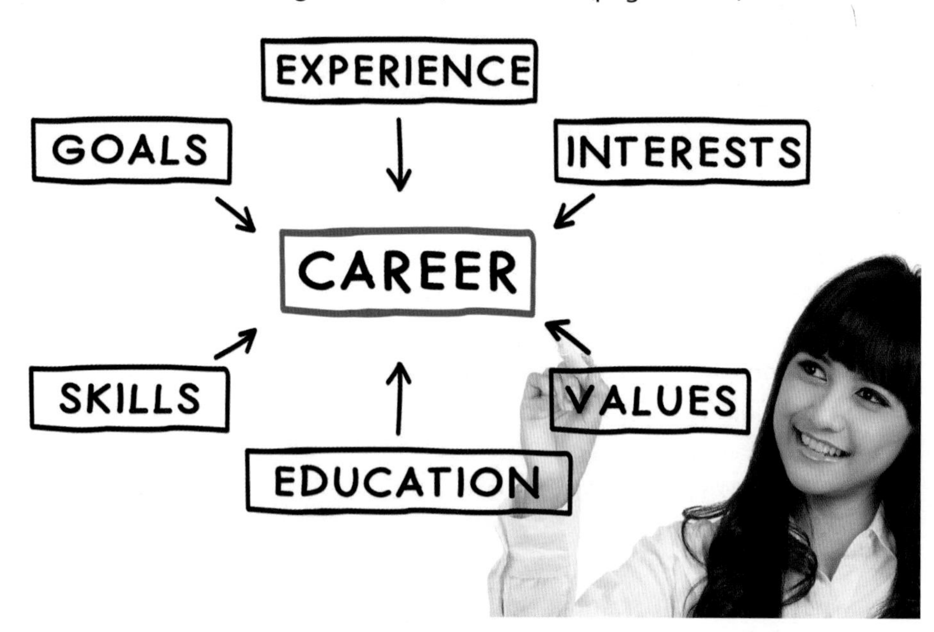

Figure 2.18 How will you develop your career?

Continuous professional development (CPD)

This term is used to describe the learning activities an individual takes part in to develop, improve and enhance their skills and knowledge. Your professional development should be regarded as life-long learning. Any job role, placement, experience, training or volunteering is a learning experience and should be regarded as professional development. Additional information about CPD can be found earlier in this unit, in Learning outcome 1, section 1.3 (page 64).

4.4 How to create a personal development plan

A personal development plan (PDP) is specific to an individual and is about how the individual plans to go about developing their personal and professional skills in order to achieve their career goals. A PDP can be used to monitor progress towards achieving those goals.

Career aspirations

Research should be carried out to find out general information about careers that interest you. This will enable you to identify the skills and qualification requirements of the type of career that you aspire to in the future.

Learning needs

It can be useful to create a chart with two columns. In the first column, list your existing skills, abilities, personal attributes and qualifications. You may have gained these through work experience, voluntary work, school or college, or even through hobbies and interests. Think of what you have gained. It might help you to talk with others, such as family members, an employer (if you have worked or completed a placement) and your friends. Often other people notice your skills and attributes more easily than you can yourself.

In the second column, list the requirements of your chosen job role. You then need to carry out a comparison of the two columns in order to identify your learning needs.

Make a list of your learning needs: these are things you want to achieve for the future in order to achieve your career aspirations. What steps are required to achieve the career you aspire to?

Short-, medium- and long-term goals

Your PDP should set goals to be achieved. The goals should lead to the career aspiration and the skills, attributes and qualifications that you have identified as needing development. The goals you set should be SMART:

- **S**pecific – a very clear statement of what needs to be done.
- **M**easurable – a statement of how you will know the goal has been achieved.
- **A**chievable – the goal should be possible to achieve, it should be something that can be done.
- **R**ealistic – the goal should be worthwhile and useful to achieve.
- **T**imely – set a specific date by which the goal should be achieved.

You will need to set a number of SMART goals to achieve your career aspirations but you will not be able to achieve all the goals at once. Instead you should try to achieve them over a period of time. There are three types of goals:

- Short-term goals – to be achieved within the next month
- Medium-term goals – to be achieved within the next four months
- Long-term goals – to be achieved within nine to twelve months.

Figure 2.19 Setting SMART goals

> **Activity**
>
> 1. Explain why this goal is not SMART: 'I will complete my work for my project by tomorrow evening.'
> 2. Write three SMART goals for completing the project: one short-term, one medium-term and one long-term.

Implementation

This means to put your plan into action by doing what you set out to achieve with the SMART goals you have set.

Review

You will need to review (look back) at the goals you set and consider the following:

- Have you achieved any of them?
- Did you achieve them on time, early or later than planned?
- Do any goals need to be changed, based on what you have achieved so far?
- Do you need to set any new goals?

Theory in action

Creating a personal development plan

Paul is 15 and wants to be a physiotherapist. He has done a work experience placement at a sports injury clinic and has observed a physiotherapist at work. Paul does not want to go into higher education to obtain a degree; instead he wants to start working straight away.

Do some research into how Paul could achieve his career aspiration, such as by doing an apprenticeship (you may find it helpful to look at the NHS Careers website (www.healthcareers.nhs.uk/career-planning/study-and-training/Apprenticeships-traineeships-and-cadet-schemes).

Questions

1. Write a list of Paul's learning needs.
2. Create a set of SMART goals that would help Paul to achieve his ambition to be a physiotherapist.

Check what you know

Give one example of the type of information about career development that you can obtain from the following sources (choose a different example for each):

1. Careers advisers
2. Internet
3. Work placement

Human growth and development through the life stages

About this unit

This unit examines the life stages from conception and birth all the way through to late adulthood. You will look at the changes and different experiences individuals have throughout their lives, and how these affect them physically, socially, emotionally and cognitively.

You will explore theories of development that try to explain the factors that influence development from childhood to adulthood.

You will explore the role of the health and social care practitioner in supporting individuals with individualised care planning through significant changes and events in their lives.

Assessment of learning grid

Grade	Learning outcome	Assessment of learning
P1	1	**Identify** the stages of development from conception to birth. **Describe** two (2) potential effects on development of: • pre-conception experiences • pre-birth experiences • birth experiences.
P2	2	**Identify** key social, emotional, cognitive and physical developmental milestones within each life stage.
P3	2	**Define** holistic development.
P4	3	**Consider** biological and environmental factors to outline the nature/nurture debate. A minimum of two (2) factors for each perspective must be given.
P5	3	**List** reasons why a health and social care practitioner responds efficiently to concerns about an individual's development.
P6	4	**Identify** transitions and significant life events at each life stage.
P7	5	**Identify** the different stages within a care-planning cycle.
M1	4	**Describe** the role of the health and social care practitioner: • in preparing individuals for a planned transition at each life stage • in supporting the needs of individuals during transition and significant life events at each life stage.
M2	5	**Explain** the purpose of each stage within an individualised care-planning cycle.
M3	5	**Use** an example to explain how an individualised care-planning cycle supports an individual's holistic needs.
D1	4	**Describe** the effects of an unplanned transition on an individual during one (1) life stage. An example must be used to support the response.
D2	3	**Summarise** the influence of nature and nurture on human development and behaviour.

Learning outcome 1: Understand development from conception to birth (P1)

High priority

Make sure you know:

- the stages of development from conception to birth
- examples of pre-conception experiences and their impact on development
- examples of pre-birth experiences and their impact on development
- examples of birth experiences and their impact on development.

1.1 Stages of development from conception to birth

The key stages of development from **conception** to birth are described below.

- **Ovulation** – occurs when an egg is released from one of the woman's ovaries and begins to travel down the fallopian tube.
- **Fertilisation** – takes place in the fallopian tube. The woman's egg is fertilised by one of the man's sperm and a baby is conceived.
- **Zygote** – the name of the cell formed by the joining of a man's sperm and a female egg (an ovum). The zygote develops into the embryo.
- **Foetus** – from eight weeks after fertilisation until birth, the embryo is called a foetus ('foetus' is Latin for 'young one').
- **Neonate** – this is the term used to describe a newborn baby, specifically a baby in the first four weeks after birth.

Figure 3.1 shows the process of conception and Table 3.1 shows the significant growth periods from conception up to birth.

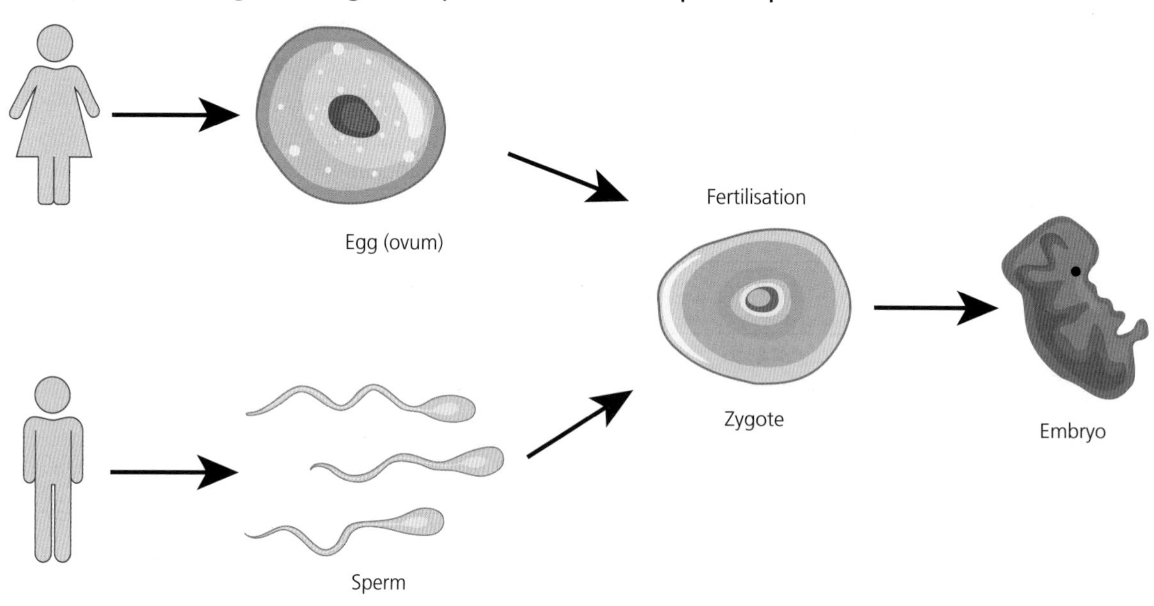

Figure 3.1 The process of conception

Table 3.1 Significant growth periods from conception to birth

Period	Effect on growth
5 weeks	• Formation of the neural tube precedes brain and spinal cord development • Blood circulation is evident • Increased heart development
6–7 weeks	• Brain growth defines distinct areas • Eyes and ears begin to develop • 'Small buds' develop – early signs of arm and leg growth
8–9 weeks	• Embryo now referred to as 'foetus' (young one) • Face slowly forming and eyes more defined • Feet and hands beginning to develop and ridges where fingers and toes will begin to appear • Major internal organs begin to develop

→

Period	Effect on growth
10–12 weeks	• Foetus is fully formed • Almost all organs and structures have formed and continue to grow until delivery • Foetus is active but mother unable to feel this movement
13–20 weeks	• Foetus is now growing rapidly • Face takes on human appearance • Hair is beginning to grow, including eyebrows and eye lashes
21–24 weeks	• Lanugo (fine, soft hair) covers the foetus • Movement may be felt by the mother
25–26 weeks	• Vigorous movement of foetus that is also responsive to touch and sound • Eyelids open
27–29 weeks	• Heartbeat strong enough to be heard using a stethoscope • Vernix (sticky protective substance) covers foetus
30–31 weeks	• Growth continues • Skin fills out, giving a plumper appearance • Lanugo and vernix disappear
32 weeks	• Baby prepares for birth
33–42 weeks	• Baby's head may 'engage'

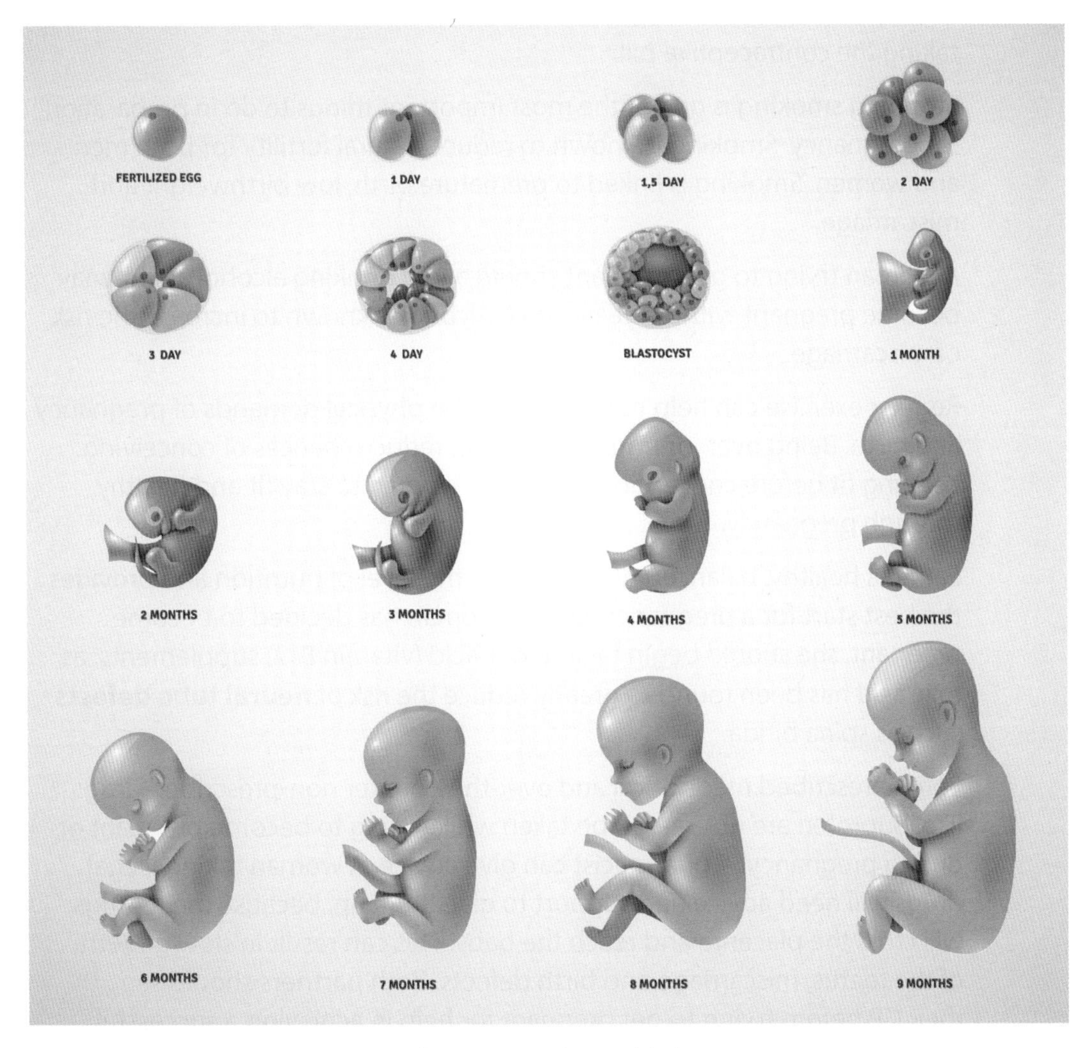

Figure 3.2 Stages of development from conception to birth

1.2 The potential effects on development of pre-conception experiences, pre-birth experiences and birth experiences

Pre-conception refers to the period of time before a woman gets pregnant; the woman may, or may not, be planning to become pregnant. **Pre-conception health** involves consideration of health, fitness and lifestyle before trying for a baby, to improve the woman's chances of becoming pregnant and to give the baby a good start. Pre-birth refers to the period during pregnancy when the foetus is in the womb.

The potential effects on development of pre-conception experiences

Maximising pre-conception health, for men and women, will create the best conditions for **conception** and the development of a healthy baby.

The method of contraception that may have been used may affect how soon pregnancy is possible. It may take from three months to a year for normal fertility to return after the contraceptive injection, and up to six months after taking the contraceptive pill.

Stopping smoking is one of the most important things to do in preparation for pregnancy. Smoking is known to reduce natural fertility for both men and women. Smoking is linked to premature birth, low birthweight and miscarriage.

A woman trying to get pregnant should avoid drinking alcohol as she may become pregnant without realising it. Alcohol is known to increase the risk of miscarriage.

Regular exercise can help to prepare for the physical demands of pregnancy and birth. Being over- or underweight can reduce chances of conceiving. Keeping fit before conception will help a woman to stay fit and healthy through pregnancy.

Eating a healthy, balanced diet improves the level of nutrition and provides the best start for a pregnancy. Once a woman has decided to become pregnant, she should begin taking folic acid (vitamin B12) supplements, as folic acid has been found to greatly reduce the risk of **neural tube defects** such as spina bifida.

Some prescribed medication and over-the-counter non-prescribed drugs like ibuprofen are not safe to be taken while trying to become pregnant or during pregnancy. A pharmacist can give advice. A woman taking illegal drugs will need advice and support to give them up, because most drugs will cross the placenta and reach the baby. This can result in slow growth of the foetus, miscarriage and birth defects. Both partners should see their GP before trying to get pregnant for help in achieving a successful conception and healthy pregnancy.

The environment can have a significant influence on an individual's health and wellbeing. The environment includes housing, local surroundings and the community. Poor housing, pollution and areas with high crime rates all have a negative impact on health and wellbeing. (For more on the impact of the environment on pre-birth experiences, see pages 116–17.)

Activity

Take a look at the BabyCentre 'Pre-pregnancy health checklist' as a starting point for learning about pre-conception experiences:

www.babycentre.co.uk/a7052/pre-pregnancy-health-checklist

Jargon buster

Conception – occurs when the egg is fertilised by a sperm.

Neural tube defect – occurs when the baby's spinal cord and spinal column do not form properly in the womb, leading to a condition called spina bifida.

Pre-conception health – involves consideration of health, fitness and lifestyle before trying for a baby, to improve the chances of becoming pregnant and to give the baby a good start.

Activity

Create a factsheet giving advice for prospective mothers covering important aspects of pre-conception health in relation to diet, exercise, alcohol, smoking, drugs and environment.

The potential effects on development of pre-birth experiences

Pre-birth experiences can have an impact on the health and safety of both the mother and the baby while in the womb.

Antenatal care

The midwife or doctor providing **antenatal care** will:

- check the health of the mother and baby
- give useful information to help the mother have a healthy pregnancy including advice about healthy eating and exercise
- discuss options and choices for care during pregnancy, labour and birth
- answer any questions the mother may have.

All expectant mothers in England are offered:

- at least two pregnancy ultrasound scans – at 8–14 weeks and 18–21 weeks
- antenatal screening tests to find out the likelihood of the baby having certain conditions such as Down's syndrome

Jargon buster

Antenatal care – 'ante' means before and 'natal' means birth, so antenatal refers to care provided throughout pregnancy up to the point of birth.

- blood tests to check for syphilis, HIV and hepatitis B
- screening for sickle cell and thalassemia, which are inherited blood disorders.

Antenatal classes are also offered, including breastfeeding workshops.

The purpose of antenatal care is to help a woman have a healthy pregnancy and be able to deliver a live, healthy baby. Mothers who have a poor diet, smoke, drink alcohol or take drugs, or who live in poor housing or rarely attend antenatal appointments are targeted by health services as they are at most risk of developing complications during pregnancy and birth.

A woman will have around seven to ten antenatal appointments during her pregnancy, which may be with a midwife, GP or at the hospital, although some women may have more appointments. The woman's medical history will be taken and her blood pressure checked; if it is high she will be told to rest to try to prevent a potentially life-threatening condition called pre-eclampsia from developing. Information will be provided about keeping healthy during pregnancy and what to expect during the birth.

Screening tests will be carried out, including ultrasound scans to monitor how the baby is developing and to check for any abnormalities (see Figure 3.3).

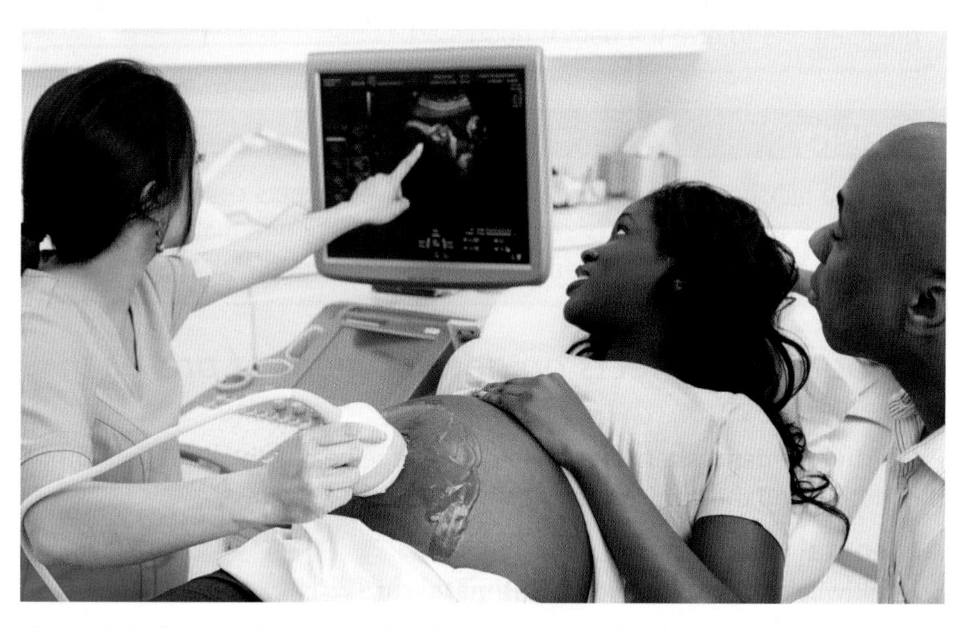

Figure 3.3 Ultrasound scans monitor how the baby is developing

Blood tests will screen the mother for conditions such as maternal diabetes or anaemia. The baby will be screened for disorders such as Down's syndrome and spina bifida. The baby's growth will be monitored throughout the pregnancy.

Attendance at antenatal appointments enables any risks to be identified and reduced where possible. It also gives the pregnant woman the opportunity to raise any concerns she may have about her pregnancy or the birth.

Figure 3.4 Couples attending an antenatal class together

Read and write

1. To read more about antenatal care and parenting classes, use the following links:
   www.nhs.uk/conditions/pregnancy-and-baby/antenatal-midwife-care-pregnant
   www.babies.uk.com
   www.nct.org.uk
2. Write about the benefits of attending antenatal and parenting classes for the mother, father and baby.

Alcohol

If a mother drinks alcohol while pregnant it can easily pass through the placenta to the baby's blood (the placenta connects the baby to the mother's blood supply). Frequent alcohol consumption during pregnancy can result in foetal alcohol syndrome (FAS). The alcohol damages important cells in the baby's body that are necessary for growth and also disrupts the connection of nerve cells. FAS results in poor growth in the womb, with a small head and jaw, and sometimes limbs are deformed. Babies born with FAS are at greater risk of having learning disabilities and potential problems with thinking, speech and memory. They may develop mood, attention or behavioural problems such as attention deficit hyperactivity disorder (ADHD), may develop problems with their liver, heart, hearing or sight and have a weakened immune system. Some babies may only have mild symptoms, while others may be severely affected. Figure 3.5 shows a baby affected by foetal alcohol syndrome.

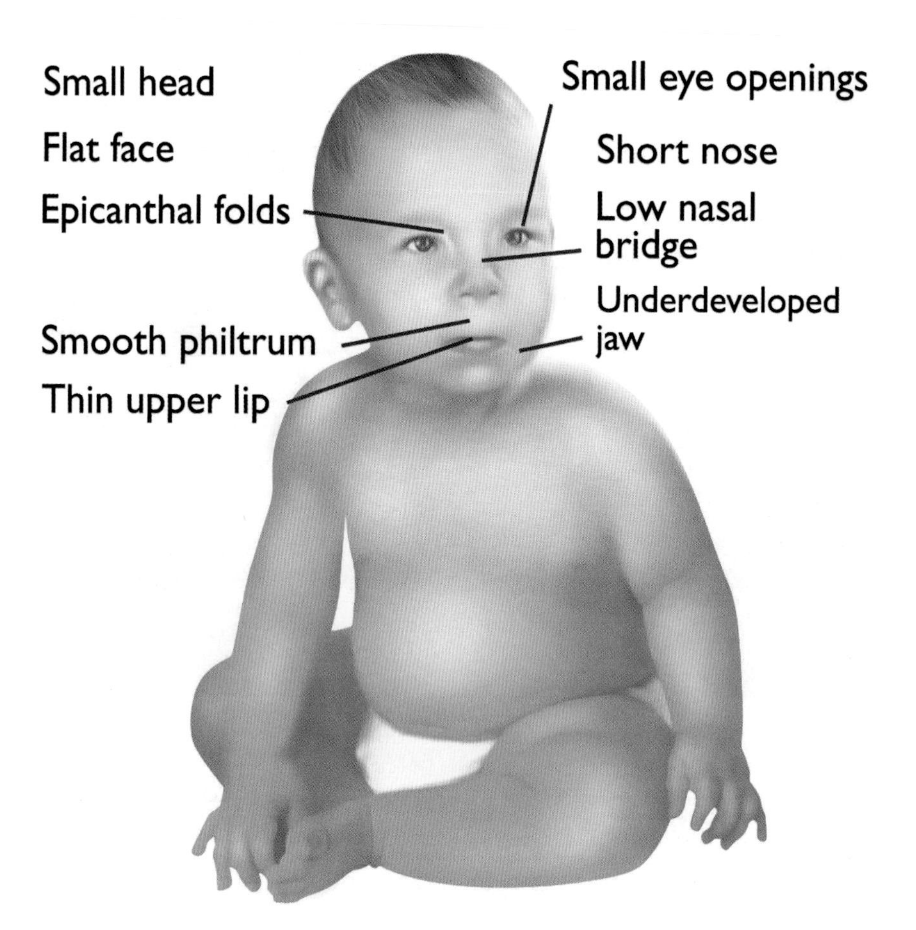

Figure 3.5 A baby affected by foetal alcohol syndrome

Jargon buster

Epicanthal folds – fold of loose skin of the upper eyelid that covers the inner corner of the eye.

Philtrum – the ridge that runs below the nose to the top lip.

Use of prescribed and non-prescribed drugs during pregnancy

Some medicines can harm the developing foetus, so a pregnant woman should always check with a pharmacist, midwife or doctor before taking medication. Even some 'natural' remedies, such as herbal, homeopathic or aromatherapy treatments, are not safe during pregnancy. A pregnant woman should check with her GP or midwife before taking any of these types of remedies. Babies born to drug addicts can experience withdrawal symptoms and may have long-term damage to their health.

Smoking

Smoking is damaging to the foetus during pregnancy, whether it is the mother who smokes or she is exposed to passive smoking from a partner, friend or family member. There is an increased risk of pregnancy complications for smokers, such as ectopic pregnancy, placental abruption, miscarriage, stillbirth and premature labour. Babies born to mothers who smoked during pregnancy are likely to be much smaller; low birth weight is one of the main causes of illness and disability in babies. Research has shown that there is a link between smoking and being born with a cleft lip and palate. Cigarettes restrict the oxygen supply to the baby so their heart has to beat harder; the chemicals from cigarettes pass into the mother's bloodstream and reach the foetus through the placenta.

Diet

Some foods need to be avoided during pregnancy as they can cause illness or harm to the baby. Unpasteurised cheese and soft blue cheese should not be eaten because they provide an ideal environment for harmful bacteria such as listeria to grow, which can cause miscarriage and stillbirth. All hard cheeses are safe to eat, providing they are made from pasteurised milk. Raw or partly cooked eggs should be avoided as they can carry toxoplasmosis which is an infection that can cause miscarriage or stillbirth. Shellfish should always be cooked, because they may contain harmful bacteria and viruses that can cause food poisoning.

Folic acid (vitamin B12) protects against developing neural tube defects such as spina bifida (see also section 1.2 (page 110). It is recommended to take 400 mg every day before and during pregnancy and to eat foods high in natural folic acid, such as leafy green vegetables and brown rice.

Health

Research has shown that unborn babies are exposed to their mother's stress hormones. This could affect the developing foetus and long-term stress can cause the mother to feel tired, depressed and make her more prone to illness. To be as stress free as possible it is important that pregnant women are supported and reassured by their family, friends and, if working, by their employers.

Find out more

Stress during pregnancy

Read more about research on this topic by following the link below.

www.theguardian.com/science/2007/may/31/childrensservices.medicineandhealth

Exercise can help to strengthen the muscles so that it is easier to carry the extra weight of pregnancy. Exercise means that joints will be stronger, circulation improves and backache may be eased, leading to a general feeling of wellbeing. Swimming is recommended and special classes such as 'yoga for pregnancy' are available in most areas.

However, exercise that involves a risk of falls such as horse riding, gymnastics and cycling should be done with caution or avoided, as a fall may risk damage to the baby. To stay safe during exercise it is recommended to drink plenty of water, avoid exercising to the point of feeling exhausted or when it is very hot, and stop straight away if feeling unwell or in pain.

Check what you know

1. Explain some features of a healthy diet when pregnant.
2. Give three reasons why attending antenatal care appointments is so important.

Theory in action

Figure 3.6 Serena

Serena is nearly six months pregnant. So far, she has not bothered to attend any antenatal care appointments as they are always at inconvenient times and it is difficult for her to get to the hospital. She enjoys smoking and likes to go out for a drink at weekends with her friends.

Describe the potential impact of Serena's lifestyle on the development of her unborn baby.

Environment

A woman's environment can have a significant influence on her health and wellbeing, before, during and after pregnancy, and can affect the baby too. Environment refers not only to the type of home in which a person lives, but also their local surroundings and community. Good conditions will have a positive impact on the health and wellbeing of children and adults alike.

Environmental factors include living:

- in overcrowded areas with no recreation spaces or facilities
- close to noisy and busy roads
- near a source of pollution
- a long way from health and welfare services.

Some areas have high crime rates which can be stressful and possibly dangerous. It may also make people afraid to go out and this can impact on their social contacts and support.

Pollution can affect health, growth and development. This includes air pollution (for example car fumes), noise pollution (such as night clubs, rowdy areas, traffic). Housing conditions such as damp, poorly maintained buildings and those with heating problems can lead to an increased risk of respiratory illnesses and stress-related illness or depression.

Complications during pregnancy

Gestational diabetes

If a pregnant mother has gestational diabetes, their diet will play an important part of managing the condition and keeping the pregnancy safe.

If the mother's blood glucose (sugar) level is high, it can cause high blood glucose levels in the baby. The baby will produce more insulin in response, just like the mother does. This can make the baby grow larger than normal which can cause difficulties during birth (see pages 119–20 for more on birth injuries due to a large baby).

In gestational diabetes, the placental hormones (i.e. those produced by the placenta) can result in a rise in blood sugar to a level that may affect the functioning of the placenta and the growth and development of the baby.

Pre-eclampsia

Most cases of pre-eclampsia are mild and have no effect on the pregnancy.

However, if left untreated, pre-eclampsia can be dangerous for both the mother and baby and increases the risk of a premature birth. Sometimes other organs, such as the liver, can become affected, and there can be problems with blood clotting.

Pre-eclampsia can sometimes progress to a more dangerous condition known as eclampsia. This can cause fits and, in severe cases, can result in the death of the mother or the baby. It is therefore vital to manage the condition safely. The focus of treatment before birth is blood pressure management; medication may also be used to control high blood pressure. With more severe pre-eclampsia, the mother is likely to be admitted to hospital. The baby is usually delivered if doctors cannot control the mother's blood pressure as the risk to the baby is small if he or she is born just a few weeks early. However, at less than 34 weeks, the decision between delivering the baby or continuing other treatment will depend on the severity of the pre-eclampsia and the risks to the mother and baby.

Find out more

Complications during pregnancy

Tommy's is a charity that funds research into the causes and prevention of pregnancy complications that lead to miscarriage, stillbirth and premature birth. They also provide pregnancy health information for parents-to-be. Use the link below to find out more.

www.tommys.org/pregnancy-information/pregnancy-complications

My life as a sonographer

My role is to carry out ultrasound scans to check how the baby is developing and to check for any abnormalities.

As a sonographer, you play an important role in the lives of your patients. You're with them as they hear their baby's heart beat for the first time. You help the doctors diagnose and treat disease. You also provide support to patients during what can be very emotional circumstances at times.

My role involves the following:

- Explaining the ultrasound procedure to patients and answering any questions they may have.
- Maintaining the ultrasound equipment and sterilising the room in which the procedure takes place.
- Spreading the ultrasound gel on the surface of the patient's body, covering the internal area being imaged.
- Performing the ultrasound and ensuring the transducer (probe) is capturing images of every angle/section that must be assessed.
- Evaluating the images for their quality, but also to interpret what is captured in the image.
- Presenting images and preliminary findings to doctors and the health care team.
- Maintaining patient records and adding medical notes related to the ultrasound procedure.

Birth experiences: complications during labour for baby and mother

Premature birth

A premature baby is one born before 37 weeks.

Causes of premature birth:

- Infection of the membranes that surround the baby, the umbilical cord and/or the amniotic fluid in the womb.
- Pre-eclampsia, which is a serious condition that only occurs during pregnancy, typically after 20 weeks. It is a combination of high blood

pressure and protein in the mother's urine. (See 'Complications during pregnancy' (page 117) for more about pre-eclampsia.)
- Multiple pregnancy, which means carrying more than one baby, normally twins.
- Placenta problems – the placenta is the baby's support system in the womb and it processes the baby's nutrients, waste and oxygen. Problems include when the placenta comes away from the wall of the womb or where it is positioned too low in the womb so it does not work properly.

Effects of premature birth:

- Premature babies have less developed immune systems and are more susceptible to infection.
- They will need help with feeding, usually through a tube, until they have developed the ability to suck and swallow themselves.
- They may need support with breathing because their lungs are not yet mature enough.
- They will need to be kept very warm to avoid hypothermia.

Lack of oxygen

A lack of oxygen to the foetus during birth may cause the baby to become distressed. This will result in the baby needing to be delivered by **caesarean section**, which is a surgical operation where the mother will either have a general or **epidural** anaesthetic.

Jargon buster

Caesarean section – a surgical procedure for delivering a baby. The baby is delivered through an incision in the mother's abdomen and uterus. The procedure can be carried out under a general anaesthetic, where the mother is unconscious, or an epidural anaesthetic, where the mother is awake but feels no pain.

Epidural – an anaesthetic administered by inserting a needle into the lower back. It is used for lower-body surgical procedures. The person remains awake but will feel no pain.

Breech birth

A baby is said to be in the breech position if it is 'bottom down' rather than 'head down'. The majority of babies who are in the breech position when labour starts are delivered by caesarean section, rather than the usual vaginal delivery.

Birth injury

This is when the baby suffers a physical injury that occurs as a result of being born. Causes can include the baby being larger than average, a long and difficult labour or a breech birth position. Being premature is also a risk as babies born before 37 weeks have more fragile bodies and may be more easily injured. Assisted delivery by forceps (large tongs) or ventouse (vacuum extraction) can cause bruising to the baby's head and face.

Babies weighing more than 4 kg (8 lb 8 oz) at birth increase the risk of:

- **birth trauma** – either the mother or baby can be affected when it is difficult for the baby to be born. Trauma may include physical symptoms, such as bone fractures or nerve damage for the baby, or tearing and severe bleeding for the mother as well as psychological distress.
- **shoulder dystocia** – this occurs when the baby's shoulder is stuck in the mother's pelvis once the head has been born. This can squash the umbilical cord, so the team need to use additional interventions to deliver the baby quickly and safely.

Large babies may have labour induced early or the mother may have to have a caesarean section so that the baby is born safely. The baby's weight will be monitored carefully in pregnancy to see whether these interventions are needed.

Check what you know

Describe two possible effects on a baby's development for each of the following:

1. Pre-conception experiences
2. Pre-birth experiences
3. Birth experiences

Five things to know

Development from conception to birth

Make sure you know:

1. the meaning of the terms 'pre-conception' and 'pre-birth'
2. reasons why antenatal care is important
3. effects on development of regular alcohol consumption, smoking and poor diet
4. the influence of the environment on a pregnant woman and her baby's health and wellbeing
5. the possible effects, on mother and baby, of complications during pregnancy.

■ Learning outcome 2: Understand development across the life span (P2, P3)

High priority

Make sure you know:

- the names and age range of the life stages
- the meaning of social, emotional, cognitive and physical development
- examples of development at each life stage.

2.1 The life stages of human development

Development happens throughout life: it does not stop when you reach adulthood. There is a generally accepted pattern of development known as 'norms' or 'milestones'. While not everyone achieves milestones at the same time, general progression through the life stages is similar. Most growth and development occurs during infancy, childhood and adolescence. Although an individual's skills and abilities become more sophisticated and complex as they progress towards adulthood, learning and development continues throughout every life stage. The key stages of the human lifespan are shown in Figure 3.7.

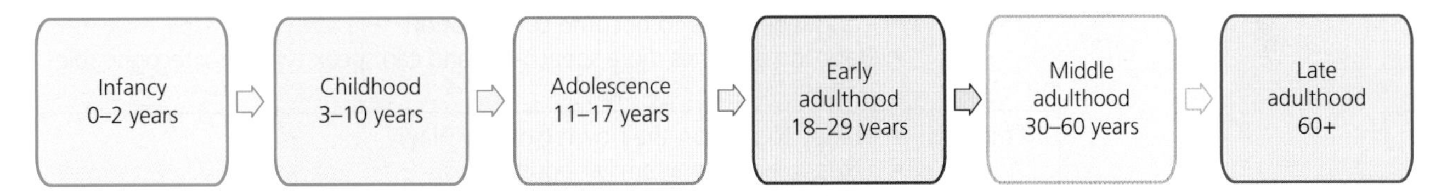

Figure 3.7 Key stages of the human lifespan

2.2 Social, emotional, cognitive and physical developments within each life stage

Social, emotional, cognitive and physical developments occur at each life stage, and are explained below.

Social development

This refers to the growth of relationships with others. It involves learning the skills and attitudes that enable individuals to live easily and comfortably with other members of their community.

Social development during infancy

There are a great number of social developments at this life stage, as shown in Table 3.2.

Table 3.2 Examples of social development during infancy

Age	Social development
Newborn	• Cries to indicate need • Imitates adults, for example facial expressions such as sticking their tongue out • Makes eye contact
1 month	• Starts to make non-crying noises such as gurgling and cooing • Crying and other noises become more expressive • Will look attentively at the carer's face when being fed
3 months	• Beginnings of conversation – will exchange 'coos' with another person • Will cry loudly to express a need • Will smile in response to being spoken to
6 months	• Enjoys playtime • Will pass toys to others • Imitates sounds and enjoys babbling • Makes a wide variety of different sounds – laughs, squeals, screams
9 months	• Prefers to be with a familiar adult • Can tell the difference between family and strangers • Copies sounds made by adults, for example animal noises, train noises • Follows simple instructions such as 'kiss Granny' • Expresses likes and dislikes at mealtimes
12 months	• Likes to be with someone they know • Imitates simple words • Language starts to become conversation • Babbling becomes more speech-like and can speak two to six recognisable words
18 months	• Happy to play on their own (solitary play) • Likes to be near a familiar adult • Wants to be independent • Can use a cup and spoon reasonably well • Enjoys repetitive stories and rhymes
2 years	• Able to feed themselves without much spillage • Plays near other children but does not play with them (parallel play) • Likes to help with chores • Engages in role-play such as putting a baby doll to bed

Social development during childhood (3–10 years)

Socialisation is the process by which we learn the norms, values and behaviour that makes us part of a particular group. There are two types of socialisation: primary and secondary socialisation.

Primary socialisation

The child's family will be the main people who contribute to his or her learned attitudes and beliefs. The child will learn the way of behaving according to the particular culture of the family in which he or she lives: this is primary socialisation.

Secondary socialisation

A child will learn from wider society as she or he meets more people and has contact with different organisations. Some of the views and opinions previously learned and accepted from their family will be questioned. This process may start when the child is at playgroup or attends nursery and continues throughout school life and work. Peer groups, the media and education are all agencies of secondary socialisation.

Examples of how agencies of socialisation could influence children's attitudes:

- family – influence of parents and siblings as role models
- media – watching/copying role models on TV, social media, etc.
- education – teachers, conformity, peers, friends, role models
- peers/friends – may imitate, desire to conform or fit in, share/learn ideas, role model influences
- religion – learn roles/beliefs/traditions.

During childhood, children often have a 'best friend', chosen because of their interests or personality. Children will also enjoy team games and will begin to understand taking turns and following rules.

Social development during adolescence (11–17 years)

- Individuals become increasingly independent of their family.
- Relationships with peer groups, close friends and others outside the individual's family become more important during adolescence.
- Fitting in by being seen in the right places, wearing the right clothes, having the right phone and listening to the right music are very important issues.
- Because of the need to fit in and belong, peer pressure sometimes makes adolescents do things because their friends do, rather than actually wanting to themselves.

Social development during adulthood (18–60+ years)

- Many adults continue friendships they made at school.
- New friendships formed at work or with parents of their children's friends.
- Retirement provides opportunity to take up hobbies and new interests and there is more time for socialising or travelling.

Read and write

Social developments

1. Reread about the social developments at each life stage.
2. Consider the impact of social development for relationhips across the life span.

Emotional development

Emotional development is about the development and expression of feelings. It involves learning how to manage emotions and displaying them appropriately as we grow older. It also includes developing **attachments** or bonds with others and feelings of belonging, as well as developing self-confidence, self-esteem and a sense of security. Emotional development is a lifelong process that involves becoming aware of your 'self', working out your feelings towards others and developing a self-image and personal identity.

Jargon buster

Attachment – refers to the emotional bond that develops between a child and their caregivers, such as parents or grandparents. It can also be an emotional bond that develops between one adult and another in an intimate relationship.

Emotional development during infancy

Table 3.3 describes the emotional developments that occur during infancy.

Table 3.3 Examples of emotional development during infancy

Age	Emotional development
Newborn	• Expresses pleasure when being cuddled, fed or bathed
1 month	• Smiles at main carer • May be described by a carer as developing a particular temperament or personality, such as lively and excitable or calm and placid
3 months	• Loves to receive attention and cuddles • Smiles at familiar people • Stares intently at carer's face when feeding and shows enjoyment when being bathed
6 months	• Gets upset when main carer leaves • Cries and laughs when others do • Wary of strangers
9 months	• Prefers to be with a familiar adult and expresses fear of strangers by crying • Enjoys songs and rhymes with actions • Enjoys games such as 'peek-a-boo'
12 months	• May have a comfort object such as a blanket or soft toy • Shows affection for family members • Likes to be with people they know • Waves good-bye
18 months	• Shows emotions clearly, such as fear, anger, happiness • Temper tantrums may occur when they cannot get their own way • Begins to use words to express own feelings
2 years	• Able to express feelings • Can be very clingy with carers • Likes to be independent and do things for themselves • Can be confident and independent

Emotional development during childhood (3–10 years)

A child learns to control his or her emotions during this life stage, including feelings of anger, jealousy and frustration. Over time the child will develop a sense of right and wrong. Most children gradually increase in self-confidence, make friendships and become more independent once they have started school. They learn to co-operate and begin to understand the viewpoints and feelings of others.

Emotional development during adolescence (11–17 years)

The hormones that affect physical development also have a big impact on an individual's emotional development at this life stage. Adolescents can experience extreme feelings and intense emotions, quickly changing from happy to upset. They may be very moody and aggressive which can make it difficult for families to deal with.

Developing a personal identity and experiencing emotional support from peers and family members is important.

Self-image and self-esteem are particularly important issues during adolescence, but also throughout adulthood. When an adolescent thinks about their self-image they often compare themselves with others. This can affect self-esteem, which influences how and what we think about ourselves.

Individuals with high self-esteem are:

- motivated to do something because they have often been successful
- confident in social situations because they usually get on well with people
- generally happy with their life
- sufficiently self-confident to cope with new challenges and to view them positively.

Individuals with low self-esteem:

- lack motivation, because when they have tried new things in the past, they may not have done very well
- lack confidence, especially when meeting new people, as they feel anxious that they will have nothing to say
- often feel unhappy
- often find life difficult and do not enjoy new challenges, as they are afraid of failure.

Adolescents who feel confident, who accept they have strengths and weaknesses and who feel loved and wanted tend not to undervalue themselves and usually have higher self-esteem.

Emotional development during adulthood (18–60+ years)

Marriage and relationships, parenthood, divorce, increasing work responsibilities, promotion or redundancy, loss of elderly parents and children leaving home are some of the major life events that happen during adulthood. Health and illness can also influence how an individual feels about their life. These issues can all have a major impact on emotions during this life stage.

Read and write

Emotional developments

1 Reread the information about emotional developments at each life stage.
2 Write about how attachment and meaningful, fulfilling relationships can support the development of self-esteem in individuals.

Cognitive development

Cognitive development refers to the development of the mind, and includes skills such as learning to talk, understanding, memory, concentration, reasoning, problem solving, imagination, reading, asking questions, telling stories, listening and following instructions.

Cognitive developments during infancy

Table 3.4 gives some examples of cognitive development during infancy.

Table 3.4 Examples of cognitive development during infancy

Age	Cognitive development
Newborn	• Begins to develop connections through the senses and growing understanding • Aware of physical sensations such as hunger and discomfort • Imitation of adults, for example facial expressions
1 month	• Will recognise primary (main) carers • Will repeat enjoyable movements • Will turn to look at the face of someone speaking
3 months	• Shows an increasing interest in playthings and their surroundings • Recognises familiar situations • Shows an understanding of cause and effect by shaking a rattle to hear its noise
6 months	• Shows understanding of words such as 'bye-bye', 'mama', dada' • Raises arms to be picked up – demonstrating understanding of cause and effect, up and down
9 months	• May say 'mum-mum', 'dad-dad' – repeats sounds, practising them • Looks for fallen/dropped toys • Looks at small objects and reaches for them • Explores objects by touching, banging, shaking • Will look for a hidden object – knows it still exists even though it cannot be seen
12 months	• When asked 'where is the ball?' they will point to the ball • Uses trial and error to learn about objects • Begins to treat or use objects in an appropriate way, such as cuddling a soft toy and using a hairbrush • Enjoys looking at picture books
18 months	• Able to recognise parts of the body • Responds to commands • Knows own name
2 years	• New words learned quickly • Asks questions constantly • Can name familiar objects, for example cat or bus

Cognitive development during childhood (3–10 years)

By the end of childhood, a child will be able to use adult speech easily and will have vastly developed their knowledge and thinking skills. During this life stage, children will:

- increase their language and understanding
- develop their vocabulary
- ask lots of questions
- express themselves in more complex ways
- read more complex stories and use this language in their writing.

Cognitive development during adolescence (11–17 years)

Abstract thinking skills develop during adolescence. This means being able to think about and apply complex ideas, such as mathematical equations, or what they would like to do in the future and how they will achieve their goals.

Cognitive development during adulthood (18–60+ years)

- Most adults use abstract thinking and problem-solving skills.
- Adults can think quickly and make reasoned, informed decisions.
- Gaining new knowledge and skills is necessary to deal with changes in employment and family life, such as looking after children.
- Thinking skills and knowledge may be further developed through education and training.
- Thinking speed and response times may slow with ageing but usually intelligence and mental ability do not.
- Older people may become wiser and may make better judgements as a result of a lifetime's experience.
- A minority of older people may develop conditions such as dementia where they lose their mental abilities.

Read and write

Cognitive developments

1. Reread the information about cognitive developments at each life stage.
2. Write an example of cognitive development at each life stage for each of these aspects:
   a) language
   b) memory
   c) reasoning
   d) thinking
   e) problem solving.

Physical development

Refers to the development of the body, such as how it gradually increases in size and also the physical skills that increase in complexity, for example from crawling to walking to running.

Physical development during infancy

Infancy is a time of rapid physical development – Table 3.5 gives some examples. At this stage, infants are developing both **fine motor skills** and **gross motor skills**.

Table 3.5 Examples of physical development during infancy

<table>
<tr><th colspan="3">Physical development</th></tr>
<tr><th>Age</th><th>Fine motor skills</th><th>Gross motor skills</th></tr>
<tr><td>Newborn</td><td colspan="2">Natural reflexes: swallowing and sucking, grasping, rooting, getting startled, walking, falling</td></tr>
<tr><td>1 month</td><td>• Opens hand and will grasp an adult's finger
• Facial expressions – shows interest and excitement</td><td>• Turns from their side to their back
• May move head towards a bright light
• Jerky, uncontrolled leg and arm movements</td></tr>
<tr><td>3 months</td><td>• Moves their head to follow adult movements
• Watches their hands and play with their fingers
• Holds a rattle briefly without dropping it</td><td>• Lifts head and chest when in the prone position (lying on their front)
• Sits with their back straight when held
• Kicks vigorously with legs</td></tr>
<tr><td>6 months</td><td>• Reaches and grabs when a small toy is offered
• Uses the whole hand (palmar grasp) to pass a toy from one hand to the other
• Explores objects by putting them in their mouth</td><td>• When held sitting or standing can do so with a straight back
• Lying on their back, can lift their legs into vertical position, grasping their feet with their hands
• Changes the angle of their body to reach out for an object
• Rolls over</td></tr>
<tr><td>9 months</td><td>• Grasps objects using finger and thumb in a pincer grasp
• Continues to explore objects by putting them in their mouth
• Releases a toy from grasp by dropping it – cannot yet put it down
• Imitates adult gestures</td><td>• Sits up unsupported, with a straight back, for a short while
• Pulls themselves into a standing position
• Stands by holding on to furniture
• May take some steps when being held
• Moves along the floor – bottom shuffling or crawling</td></tr>
<tr><td>12 months</td><td>• Points at interesting objects with index finger
• Throws and drops toys deliberately
• Builds with a few bricks
• Releases a small object into another person's hand</td><td>• Now mobile, so can probably walk alone with feet wide apart or with one hand held
• Rises to a sitting position from lying down
• May crawl upstairs or onto low items of furniture</td></tr>
<tr><td>18 months–2 years</td><td colspan="2">• Climbs stairs with support
• Climbs stairs one at a time
• Runs
• Throws a ball but cannot catch it yet</td></tr>
</table>

Jargon buster

Fine motor skills – smaller movements such as those required to grasp a pen or hold a paintbrush.

Gross motor skills – larger movements of the legs, arms, feet or the whole body.

Physical development during childhood (3–10 years)

- Children continue to grow steadily, though not at the same pace as during infancy.
- Motor skills continue to develop – by four years old, most children can throw and kick a large ball.
- By six or seven years, a child can skip and ride a bicycle.
- Children will develop increased body strength and co-ordination.
- At eight or nine years, children will begin to join letters together in handwriting.
- Children will often enjoy participating in active games and sports.

Physical development during adolescence (11–17 years)

Physical development in adolescence is called puberty. It is a stage where the child's body turns into that of an adult. There are physical, hormonal and sexual changes and the body becomes capable of reproduction. There is also a 'growth spurt' which involves the fast growth of bones and muscles. The effects of puberty for girls and boys are described in Table 3.6.

Table 3.6 Effects of puberty

Girls	Boys
Reproductive organs grow: ovaries, uterus and vagina	Testicles and penis grow
Breasts develop and hips widen	Voice 'breaks' – becomes deeper
Menstruation starts	Facial hair begins to grow
Growth of pubic and underarm hair	Growth of pubic and underarm hair
Increase in body sweat as the sweat glands become more active	Increase in body sweat as the sweat glands become more active
Acne may develop	Acne may develop

Physical development during adulthood (18–60+ years)

Table 3.7 describes the physical changes that occur as we age.

Table 3.7 Physical effects of the ageing process

Part of the body affected	Ageing effects
Eyesight	• Cataracts and glaucoma may develop; may cause blindness if left untreated
Hair	• Hair starts to thin, growth slows and men may go bald • Hair turns grey or white
Hearing	• Deteriorates, as an individual loses quiet and high pitched sounds • A hearing aid may become necessary
Heart	• Becomes less efficient • Blood pressure may increase • Blood vessels become less elastic and this can lead to stroke or heart attack
Lungs and respiratory system	• Lungs become less elastic and the respiratory muscles weaken • May be less able to exercise due to reduced lung function • Important to be vaccinated against flu and pneumonia as more susceptible to developing these illnesses
Reproductive system	• Menopause means the end of menstruation; this may cause unpleasant side effects such as hot flushes and disturbed sleep
Skeleton and muscles	• Loss of height • Reduction in bone mass • Women in particular can develop osteoporosis, which increases the risk of fractures • Problems with knee and hip joints can cause mobility problems. Muscles become less flexible and balance can be affected
Skin	• Loss of elasticity • Wrinkles develop
Urinary system	• Kidneys become less efficient at filtering waste products; may need to pass urine more frequently

Check what you know

Identify whether the following statements describe an aspect of infant and children's physical, cognitive or social development:

1. Smiles in response to an adult
2. Rides a tricycle
3. Follows a simple instruction
4. Re-tells familiar stories
5. Sits without support
6. Eager to be independent, for example 'me do it'

2.3 Holistic development

Holistic development refers to how the child or adult develops as a whole being since all aspects of development are taking place at the same time and are linked. Developments do not occur in isolation; they are interrelated with one aspect of development impacting on another. For example, when a child can use language effectively they will have more opportunities for social interaction. Reading a story with a child can involve pointing at pictures, facial expressions and bonding with the person reading the story. In this way, many aspects of development are involved.

Five things to know

Development across the life stages

Make sure you know:

1. the name and age range of the key life stages
2. examples for each life stage of each type of development – social, emotional, cognitive and physical
3. the difference between 'primary' and 'secondary' socialisation
4. the key terms 'attachment', 'self-esteem', 'gross motor skills' and 'fine motor skills'
5. the meaning of 'holistic' development.

Learning outcome 3: Understand influences on human development (P4, P5, D2)

High priority

Make sure you know:

- the meaning of the terms 'nature' and 'nurture'
- examples of biological factors that influence development
- examples of environmental influences on development.

3.1 The nature versus nurture debate in relation to human behaviour and development

Nature refers to an individual's development and behaviour being the result of inherited characteristics they were born with. Nurture refers to an individual's development and behaviour being a result of learning from environmental influences and the people around them.

Nature factors are internal influences from within the body, such as genes, inherited characteristics and biological influences, whereas nurture involves external influences from the environment. These environmental factors can have a very powerful effect on development. For example, poor housing conditions and not having enough food to eat are environmental factors that can lead to poor growth in children and illness in people at any life stage.

An individual's growth and development is influenced by both nature and nurture – the discussion about which is more influential is called the nature–

nurture debate. People do in fact develop through the combined effects of nature *and* nurture. However, one may be considered to have more influence than the other, particularly in cases such as an inherited disease that is life limiting. Nature cannot be changed whereas the ways people are nurtured can be.

Extend

For each of the following, consider whether you think the *main* influence on the person's development or behaviour is 'nature' or 'nurture':

1. Michael is an alcoholic. His father was an alcoholic.
2. Statistics show that men commit most of the violent crimes in the UK.
3. Barinder has developed lung cancer.
4. Sarah lived to the age of 102.

Share your thoughts with a friend and discuss your ideas. Is it possible to reach a conclusion? Is nature or nurture more influential?

3.2 Factors which may influence human development

A wide range of factors influence our development, as described below.

Biological influences

Genes contain the information and instructions that control the development of living organisms. Genes influence individual differences, such as gender, hair and eye colour, height and skin colour. As we learn more about genetics it is becoming widely accepted that genetic influences interact and are interlinked with environmental influences. This means, for example, that genetics and external environment factors influence how we develop. For example, genetics may influence the development of our physiology and, in turn, our behaviour; however, our genes do not directly control our actions.

Down's syndrome

Down's syndrome is a condition caused by having one additional chromosome. Children with Down's have similar physical features and have some degree of learning disability, but this varies in individual children. Life expectancy is reduced.

Cystic fibrosis

Cystic fibrosis (CF) is caused by a faulty gene that results in the body producing mucus that clogs up the lungs and other organs. It results in impaired lung function and can lead to reduced growth, due to the effects on the digestive system. Regular physiotherapy is required and CF patients tend to suffer from frequent lung infections that result in hospital stays. Emotional, intellectual and social development may be affected as schooling and social interaction is disrupted.

Lifestyle and health

How someone chooses to live their life can have a huge impact on their health and wellbeing. Choosing to drink alcohol, smoke or take drugs will have a negative effect on an individual's development and health. Choosing a healthy diet and not drinking excessive alcohol are positive choices which will promote holistic health.

Education

An engaging education can have a very positive influence on a person's whole life as it increases their chances of finding employment satisfaction, which can raise self esteem. A healthy disposition to learning is positive for children as they learn new skills, make new friends and become independent. This gives them confidence and a sense of achievement.

Employment

There are many benefits to mental health and self-development for individuals who enjoy their work and find it fulfilling, interesting and worthwhile. They will often gain a sense of achievement and success in their lives, which benefits their overall health and wellbeing.

Socio-economic

Socio-economic factors relate to the level of income a person has and how this in turn affects their housing, health, education, environment and access to services. Income is received from paid work, benefits, savings or pensions.

Relationships

Belonging to a family can have many advantages: it can provide a safe, loving home and provide a caring environment for a child to be brought up in. A family can help throughout life and can be there to provide practical or financial support when needed. Being with a family and having someone to talk to may reduce stress which is positive, but it can also increase stress. If there are arguments about family issues or about money it can cause a lot of tension for family members. Sometimes family life can be impacted by stressful circumstances that present challenges. These are usually short term, but long-term challenges may require formal intervention.

Friendships provide company, enjoyment and shared good times. They can also be a great support in bad times. If older adults have friends this can provide stimulation through shared interests and keeping each other company, preventing loneliness and depression in later life.

Working relationships can be very positive if you are made to feel you are a valued member of the team. However, sometimes work relationships are not good and can have a negative impact on an individual's life. It can be hard to manage if you are not appreciated or, in some cases, are bullied or taken advantage of.

Culture

Many people are influenced by the media, which can have both possitive and negative effects. Social media has contributed to unrealistic beauty standards, which can place pressure on individuals. However, television can be a positive influence: documentaries inform and inspire people and may introduce children to new career ideas.

Different cultures sometimes clash as not everyone understands the ways and traditions of other cultural groups. Sometimes this can lead to family problems between generations of the same culture, as parents may have different expectations from their children as to how to live their lives.

Physical environment

A clean and safe local environment offers a safe setting for children to play, explore and make friends. Inadequate housing creates stress and damages an individual's physical and mental health as the conditions may be poor. For example, overcrowded housing may make it difficult to study and do homework.

Bullying

This can be cyber bullying, emotional distress or physical bullying and it can have a very significant impact on an individual's self-esteem. This can cause them to suffer anxiety, a loss of concentration and may even lead to physical harm if the bully injures the person or the victim begins self-harming. Bullying can have a major impact on a person and may prevent them attending school or work.

Aspiration

Good educational experiences and a supportive family will promote a child's development and open their minds to the many opportunities in life, helping them to aspire to achieve success. A lack of a good education may mean a child will not have the skills required to obtain employment: adults without basic skills are more likely to be unemployed. Having aspirations is the first step to achieving them, rather than drifting through life unsure of what to do next.

Theory in action

Alex and Molly

Molly is three years old. She lives with her mother, Alex, who is aged 19 and a single mother. Molly has no brothers or sisters. Alex does not work, but is hoping to start a college course in the near future. Alex's income consists of income support, child benefit and housing benefit. Molly's maternal grandparents live nearby and she sees them several times a week. Molly lives in a two-bedroom terraced house, with a small back yard, which is rented from the local housing association.

The house is situated on a busy main road. The local amenities are quite good, with small shops and a supermarket within walking distance. Molly's house is on a bus route, with buses travelling to the town centre and to →

the local hospital. There is a health centre in the village, a primary school and a Sure Start Children's Centre. Molly is due to start nursery in two weeks' time and currently goes to a mums and toddlers group every week.

Questions

1 Identify and explain the negative environmental factors that may influence Molly's development.
2 Describe factors that will benefit Alex and Molly.

Five things to know

Influences on human development

Make sure you know:

1 the difference between 'nature' and 'nurture', and examples of how each can influence development
2 examples of biological factors that can affect an individual's development
3 how relationships can impact development
4 how education can influence an individual's development
5 how socio-economic factors can impact an individual's development.

3.3 Reasons for recognising and responding to concerns regarding individuals' development

Figure 3.8 explains the reasons for recognising and responding to concerns about an individual's development. Some of the reasons when, why and how to respond are described below.

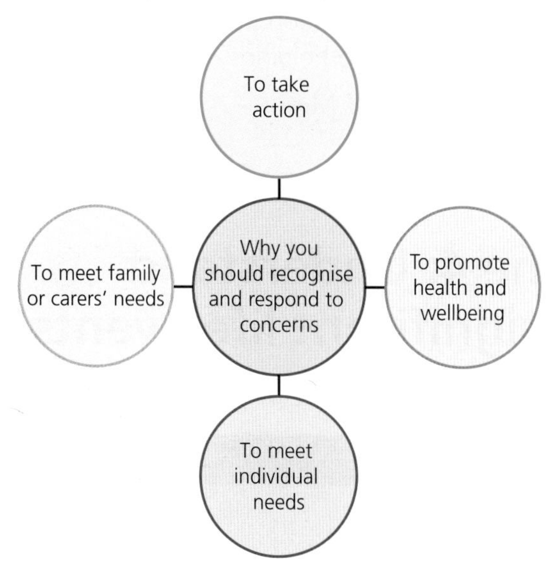

Figure 3.8 Recognising and responding to concerns

When:

- A child seems not to be thriving.
- There are unexplained injuries on a child or adult.

- Self-neglect is evident.
- Signs of neglect or abuse.
- Changes in behaviour.
- Bullying is suspected.

Why:

- Duty of care.
- To support the individual who is a cause for concern.
- To provide appropriate care or treatment.
- To investigate the concern.
- To obtain or provide information.
- To reassure carers/family/friends.
- To prevent neglect or abuse.

How:

- Follow workplace policies and procedures.
- Inform the designated safeguarding officer.
- Inform senior staff/family.
- Inform the regulatory body.

Read and write

Lucy is on a nursery placement. She is concerned about Mason who is three years old. Mason is behind in his developmental progress and is not near the expected height for his age. He is the youngest of three children. Mason's dad left home before he was born and Mason never sees him now. Mason is often collected late and by different people. He is very clingy with Lucy and always wants her attention. Mason enjoys his meals and eats well, usually asking for second helpings.

1 Write a list of concerns you might have about Mason.
2 Explain what Lucy should do in this situation.

Learning outcome 4: Understand transitions and significant life events (P6, M1, D1)

High priority

Make sure you know:

- the transitions and significant life events at each life stage
- short- and long-term impacts of transitions
- the effects of transitions on emotions, relationships, independence, health and resilience.

4.1 Transitions and significant life events across the life stages

Transitions means changes. As individuals pass through the various stages in their lives they experience many different transitions. Transitions are a normal part of growing up and maturing through life. Some are expected or planned, such as starting school, while others are unexpected, such as illness. Examples for each life stage are shown below.

Infancy (0–2 years)

- Weaning
- Separation
- Toilet training
- Moving from being home all day to starting at nursery (leaving primary carer for first time)
- Birth of a sibling

Childhood (3–10 years)

- Starting school
- Learning to read
- Birth of a sibling
- Moving house
- Being taken into care

Adolescence (11–17 years)

- Transfer to secondary school
- Taking exams
- Puberty
- Boyfriend/girlfriend
- Leaving home
- Driving test

Figure 3.9 Passing exams can have a long-term impact on your life

Early adulthood (18–29 years)

- Go to university
- Leave home
- First job
- Exams
- Get married
- Become a parent

Middle adulthood (30–60 years)

- Get married
- Become a parent
- Unemployment
- Change job
- Promotion
- Move to a new house
- Loss of parents
- Menopause
- Divorce and family break-up

Late adulthood (60+ years)

- Retirement
- Move to a new house – downsizing
- Age-related medical conditions
- Move into residential care
- Family illness/disability
- Bereavement

Check what you know

Identify two planned and two unplanned transitions for each life stage.

Activity

Make a list of the transitions and life events that you have experienced.

4.2 The impact that transitions and significant life events may have on individuals

Short- and long-term impacts

Short-term impacts are those that affect a person for a few days or weeks. Long-term impacts will affect a person over several months or even years.

Impacts, both short and long term, can have an effect on an individual's emotions, relationships, independence, health and resilience.

Emotional

Emotional impacts will depend on whether the individual is happy with what has happened or not. The birth of a planned baby will bring much joy, whereas being diagnosed with a serious illness will be devastating.

Relationship changes

Relationships can bring a sense of belonging, love, security and happiness, but a negative experience that leads to a divorce is likely to make an individual wary of starting a new relationship. They may lack trust and not want to get involved with anyone for a long time. Friendships, working and professional relationships can all change and be affected by events.

Being diagnosed with a long-term illness means an individual may require help and support with many tasks of daily living. It can become difficult to maintain independence and carry on with daily routines and relationships. A person may have to give up their job and rely on their partner or other family members to help with daily living tasks such as bathing and dressing, shopping, cleaning and washing. This causes their partner to become a carer and so the relationship undergoes a significant change.

Independence

Starting school or nursery, starting a new job and being promoted are generally approached with mixed emotions, excitement and anticipation, but individuals will probably be nervous or anxious too, when going through this type of life event. Children may feel very 'grown up' and independent when starting school, though younger children starting nursery may take time to get used to their independence away from mum or dad.

Having treatment for an illness may cause loss of independence for a while or even permanently, depending on the illness. The individual may have to rely on someone to take them to the hospital for treatment every week, for example.

Health

A serious illness can be a major and completely unexpected event in someone's life at any stage. The treatment for serious illnesses such as cancer or heart disease can have very long-term effects on individuals and can be both a positive, and a negative, impact: treatment may improve, or remove completely, the illness, which is a positive impact. Having treatment that works makes the person feel better and more in control of their life because they feel they can do something about their illness that has beneficial results. This can improve an individual's state of mind as well as their health and wellbeing.

However, there can be negative side effects of many treatments, such as hair loss, constant nausea or weight gain for example, or the treatment could be painful and tiring to endure, such as physiotherapy or chemotherapy sessions. Treatment can sometimes be for a short time or may be longer term or for the rest of an individual's life. Having to endure complex treatment in the long term can cause feelings of stress or depression, especially if there are unpleasant side effects. Individuals may feel more ill by having the necessary treatment but fear the consequences if they do not endure it.

Resilience

This refers to an individual's ability to recover quickly from difficulties or setbacks. It is the process of adapting to a new situation that may not have been the person's choice, such as redundancy or family and relationship problems. Resilience means being able to 'bounce back' and recover from difficult experiences.

Activity

Using the list you made of your transitions for the activity on page 138, describe the short- and long-term impacts you experienced.

Check what you know

Describe the short- and long-term impacts of an unplanned transition in the middle adulthood life stage.

Extend

Think about a time when you were ill – for example, with a cold or flu, a broken arm or nausea. Ask yourself the following questions:

- How did your usual daily life change while you were ill?
- Were there things you could not do for a while?
- Were there things you had to do differently?
- Did someone else have to help you do things you usually do for yourself?
- Did you have to take a course of medication or have treatment of some kind? Did it have side effects?
- How did it affect your emotional, social and mental wellbeing?

Five things to know

Transitions and major life events and their impact on individuals

Make sure you know:

1. that some transitions are planned and others are unexpected and that you are able to recognise examples of both
2. examples of transitions and major life events at each life stage
3. how an individual's independence can be affected by life events
4. how 'resilience' can help an individual to cope with planned and unexpected life events
5. short- and long-term impacts of relationship changes.

4.3 The role of the health and social care practitioner in preparing individuals for a planned transition and supporting the needs of individuals during transition and significant life events

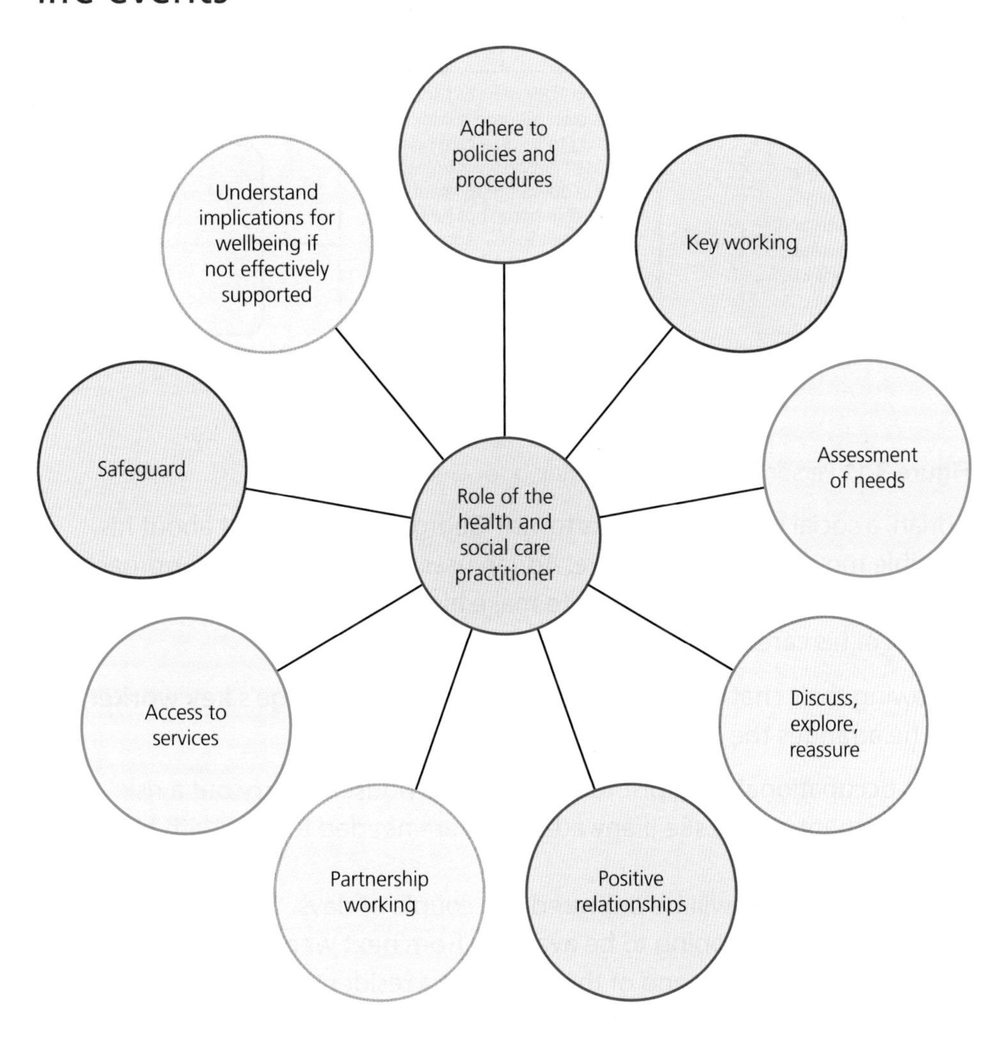

Figure 3.10 The role of the health and social care practitioner

Person-centred care means working together with the individual to plan their care and support to meet their unique needs. The individual is able to control how they want their care and support to be.

Active participation describes a way of working that makes sure an individual can take part in the activities and relationships of everyday life as independently as possible. They are an active partner in their own care and support.

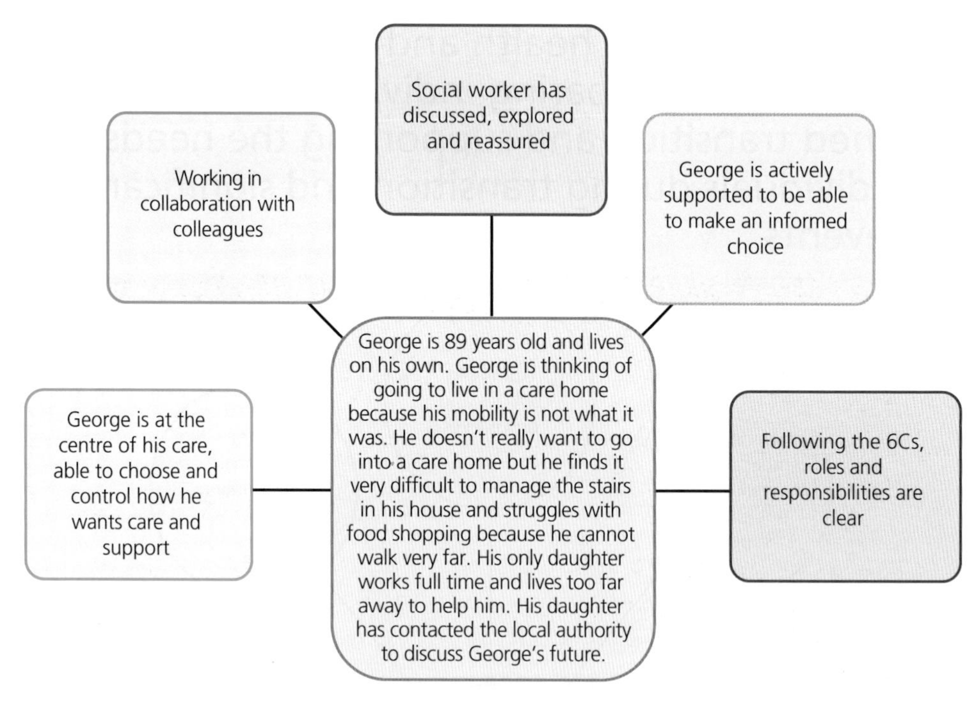

Figure 3.11 Person-centred care planning for George

Adrian, a social worker, arranges to visit George to have a chat about his possible move to residential care. Adrian uses a person-centred approach to ensure that George is supported to make his choices and is involved and in control of his care.

Following their chat, it is agreed that Adrian will be George's **key worker**, and he arranges the following care package:

- An occupational therapist to visit George's house to carry out a risk assessment and to see if any adaptions are needed to help with his mobility.
- A walking frame will be delivered in a couple of days.
- Help with his shopping to be available from next week.
- A week's stay, at the end of the month, at a residential home George is interested in, so he can try it out and see if he likes it. This is to help inform his choice of whether to stay at home or move into residential care.
- The situation to be reviewed when George returns home from his care home stay.

Jargon buster

Key worker – a person who is assigned to an individual service user and who becomes their first point of contact. He or she is responsible for communicating with the wider health and social care teams to ensure that the needs of the service user are met, for example ensuring they have the equipment they need to enable them to be mobile.

Learning outcome 5: Understand the role of care planning in meeting the needs of individuals and promoting wellbeing (P7, M2, M3)

High priority

Make sure you know:

- the purpose of care planning
- how individualised care planning meets holistic needs
- the stages in the care planning cycle.

A care plan is a tool used to ensure that an individual's care and support needs are met. The care plan is developed with the involvement of the individual along with the practitioners, care services and organisations that will be providing care. The individual's family, and any friends who may provide informal care, are also involved. Care plans should be agreed with the individual or their representative if, for example, they have a condition such as dementia which affects their ability to make decisions. Care plans should clearly identify the type of care required, who will be responsible for providing it and when. Care plans need to be reviewed regularly to ensure that they still meet the individual's care needs, which may change over time.

5.1 Purpose of individualised care planning

There are a number of reasons why individualised care planning is used, including:

- identifying individual needs
- recognising support needs
- action planning and goal setting
- risk management
- ensuring consistency of care
- maintaining continuity of care.

(See also the example of person-centred planning for George in Figure 3.11 on page 142.)

5.2 Care planning cycle

A care or support plan is a good way to work out how an individual's care needs will be met, including the roles and responsibilities of all those involved.

The stages of the care planning cycle are:

- person-centred (see the example of person-centred planning for George in Figure 3.11, on page 142)
- assess – risks, needs
- implement – carry out the plan
- monitor – regular checks to know if the plan is working
- review – consider the care put in place: does it meet the individual's needs?
- revise – make any changes highlighted by the review.

Check what you know

Write a definition of the term 'care plan'.

Extend

Choose one of the following individuals:

- an older adult who has just been diagnosed with dementia
- a 35-year-old who has just returned home from hospital, his legs have been injured in a car accident

Produce a care plan for that individual. The plan should include:

- **Needs of the individual** – what does the individual want to achieve? For example, pain relief, improved mobility, social interaction, feeling safe, going back to work.
- **Wishes and preferences** – for example, does the individual want care at home, in a hospital, GP surgery, or residential care home?
- **Risks** – is the individual safe, at risk of falls, poor mobility, able to take medication as prescribed, prepare meals and eat healthily?
- **Type of care required to meet needs** – for example, does the individual need practitioners, special equipment or aids, transport to the care setting, help with daily living activities, meals provided?
- **When and where the care is to be provided** – every day, week or month? Practitioners visiting the home, trips to a day centre, at a local clinic?

GLOSSARY

Adhere – to follow instructions or rules exactly as required.

Anaesthetist – a doctor who specialises in pain relief.

Antenatal care – 'ante' means before and 'natal' means birth, so antenatal refers to care provided throughout pregnancy up to the point of birth.

Arthritis – a condition that causes pain, swelling and inflammation in the joints.

Attachment – refers to the emotional bond that develops between a child and their caregivers, such as parents or grandparents. It can also be an emotional bond that develops between one adult and another in an intimate relationship.

Attributes – a quality or a characteristic that someone has, for example confidence, cheerfulness, trustworthiness, a willingness to learn.

Behaviours – the way in which someone acts or conducts themselves in response to a particular situation or person, for example co-operatively, with commitment, calmly.

Bereavement – the period following the loss of a loved one, such as a friend, partner, wife, husband, parent or child.

Best practice – procedures or ways of working that are accepted as being the best and most effective methods to use.

British Sign Language (BSL) – the use of hand movements, gestures, body language and facial expressions to communicate. BSL is used by individuals who are deaf or have a hearing impairment.

Caesarean section – a surgical procedure for delivering a baby. The baby is delivered through an incision in the mother's abdomen and uterus. The procedure can be carried out under a general anaesthetic, where the mother is unconscious, or an epidural anaesthetic, where the mother is awake but feels no pain.

Care Quality Commission (CQC) – a government organisation responsible for checking standards in health and social care settings.

Chronic – refers to an illness or condition that lasts longer than three months and that is ongoing; the illness can be controlled but not cured.

Client – an individual who accesses a health or social care service.

Client group – a group of individuals accessing a health or social care service.

Coeliac disease – a disease in which the body's immune system mistakes substances such as gluten in food as a threat and attacks them, leading to symptoms that can cause severe discomfort.

Commissioning – the process of planning and agreeing services that are needed.

Competency – having the ability or skills to do something correctly.

Conception – occurs when the egg is fertilised by a sperm.

Confidentiality – limits access or places restrictions on sharing certain types of sensitive information, such medical records, so that it is kept private and available only to those who need to be aware of it.

Control measures – actions that can be taken to reduce the risks posed by a hazard or to remove the hazard altogether.

Culture – the traditions, customs, beliefs or values that are shared by a group in society.

Development – the process of learning skills, e.g. movement, language, thinking, feelings.

Direct discrimination – intentionally putting someone at a disadvantage or treating them unfairly based on their age, gender or race, for example.

District nurse – supports the general needs of the local community, providing care at home for someone discharged from hospital, or an older person recovering from a fall. They also have additional training in public health, which enables them to support the health needs of at-risk or deprived individuals, including the homeless, addicts or travellers, to promote good health and prevent illness.

Domiciliary care – care and support provided for an individual in their own home (also known as home care).

Dynavox – speech-generating software that converts text, pictures and symbols on a screen into speech when touched.

Empathetic – having an understanding of other people's feelings.

Epicanthal folds – fold of loose skin of the upper eyelid that covers the inner corner of the eye.

Epidural – an anaesthetic administered by inserting a needle into the lower back. It is used for lower-body surgical procedures. The person remains awake but will feel no pain.

Fine motor skills – smaller movements such as those required to grasp a pen or hold a paintbrush.

Formal care – provided by, for example, statutory services such as a hospital, GP surgery or the local authority. Staff are qualified or trained and are employed to provide their services.

Gross motor skills – larger movements of the legs, arms, feet or the whole body.

Growth – a physical increase in size.

Harassment – unwanted behaviour that is intended to intimidate or humiliate someone.

Health visitor – a qualified and registered nurse who works in the community to monitor the development of babies and children.

Hearing loop – a special type of sound system for use by people with hearing aids. The hearing loop provides a wireless signal that is picked up by the hearing aid and can greatly improve the quality of sound while reducing background noise.

IBS (irritable bowel syndrome) – a disorder where food moves through the digestive system too quickly or too slowly, causing cramps, bloating and other symptoms.

Indirect discrimination – when a policy, practice or a rule applies to everybody but has a detrimental effect on some people. For example, if a job advert stated that male applicants must be clean shaven, this would discriminate aganist individuals whose religious beliefs require them to have a beard.

Individual – a person, man, woman or child accessing health or social care.

Informal care – provided by individuals who are not paid to do so, such as family, friends, neighbours and volunteers.

Inspection – the process of carrying out checks to see whether services provided meet the required standards.

Key worker – a person who is assigned to an individual service user and who becomes their first point of contact. He or she is responsible for communicating with the wider health and social care teams to ensure that the needs of the service user are met, for example ensuring they have the equipment they need to enable them to be mobile.

Lightwriter – a text-to-speech device that allows a message to be typed on a keyboard, displayed on a screen and then converted into speech.

Local – refers to a particular area

Makaton – the use of speech, gestures and pictures to communicate with individuals who have learning and communication difficulties.

Manual handling – using the correct procedures when physically moving any load by lifting, putting down, pushing or pulling; for example, transferring a client from a chair into bed.

National – refers to the whole country.

National Institute for Health and Care Excellence (NICE) – assesses new drugs and treatments to establish their effectiveness for patients and whether they are cost effective for supply by the NHS. Drugs and treatments are only available on the NHS if they have been approved by NICE.

Neural tube defect – occurs when the baby's spinal cord and spinal column do not form properly in the womb, leading to a condition called spina bifida.

Obstetrician – a doctor specialising in the care of pregnant women and who will deliver the baby if there are complications.

Ofsted – the government organisation that inspects social care services that care for children and young people and also any services providing education and skills training for learners of all ages.

Osteoporosis – a loss of bone density which leads to weakened bones that fracture easily.

Person-centred care – focusing care on the needs of the individual. Ensuring that people's needs are met and they can make informed decisions about their care.

Philtrum – the ridge that runs below the nose to the top lip.

Podiatrist – provides foot care such as removing corns and hard skin and ingrowing toe nails.

Pre-conception health – involves consideration of health, fitness and lifestyle before trying for a baby, to improve the chances of becoming pregnant and to give the baby a good start.

Prioritise – deciding the order for dealing with several tasks according to their importance.

Protected characteristic – refers to nine characteristics of individuals identified by the Equality Act. It is unlawful to discriminate on the basis of a protected characteristic.

Redress – to put something right, for example an individual obtaining justice after receiving inadequate care. Redress may take the form of compensation awarded by the courts or the individual having their rights restored in some way.

Regulator – an independent organisation that carries out inspections to monitor and rate the quality of services provided.

Reminiscence therapy – this involves the use of photographs, music and familiar objects to enable an individual to talk about and share their past life experiences. It is often used with individuals who have dementia, supporting them to interact with others.

Risk assessment – the process of evaluating the likelihood of a hazard causing harm.

Safeguarding – actions taken to protect individuals by facilitating a safe and healthy environment.

Service user – an individual who accesses a health or social care service.

Skills – having the ability to do specific tasks well.

Sonographer – a health professional who is specially trained to carry out ultrasound scans.

Transparency – not concealed, hidden or covered up; the inspections show things exactly as they are, whether it is good or not.

INDEX